CGP

Give yourself a high five with CGP!

If you're aiming for a Grade 4 or 5 in GCSE Maths, you'll need to be ready for anything the exams can throw at you. Ready like a hawk.

That's where this brilliant CGP book comes in. It's packed with questions that are just like the trickiest ones from the Foundation Level papers. If you can answer all these, you'll be laughing when it comes to the real thing.

We've also included step-by-step answers, so if you drop any marks, it's easy to find out exactly where you went wrong.

CGP — still the best! ☺

Our sole aim here at CGP is to produce the highest quality books — carefully written, immaculately presented and dangerously close to being funny.

Then we work our socks off to get them out to you — at the cheapest possible prices.

Contents

✓ Use the tick boxes to check off the topics you've completed.

Section Five — Shapes and Area

Section Six — Angles and Geometry

Section Seven — Probability and Statistics

Published by CGP

Editors:
Michael Bushell, David Ryan, Michael Weynberg

With thanks to Helen Kennedy and Glenn Rogers for the proofreading.

Clipart from Corel®
Printed by Elanders Ltd, Newcastle upon Tyne

Based on the classic CGP style created by Richard Parsons.

Exam Tips

Exam Stuff

1) For your GCSE Mathematics course you will have <u>three</u> exams
— one non-calculator exam and two calculator exams.

2) Each exam is 1 hour 30 minutes long and is worth <u>80 marks</u>.

3) Timings in the exam are really important, so here's a quick guide...

- As each paper is worth <u>80 marks</u> and you've got <u>90 minutes</u> to complete the paper, you should spend about a <u>minute per mark</u> working on each question (i.e. 2 marks = 2 mins).

- The <u>hardest questions</u> will come towards the end of each exam and are often worth the <u>most marks</u>, so give yourself plenty of time to tackle them.

- Use any spare time at the end of the exam to <u>check</u> back through your answers and make sure you haven't made any silly mistakes. <u>Not</u> to daydream about snacks.

Here are a Few Handy Hints

1) **Don't let <u>easy marks</u> slip through your fingers.**
To give yourself the best chance of getting the highest grades you'll need to cut out as many <u>silly mistakes</u> as possible. <u>Read the question</u> properly, give your answer to the right <u>degree of accuracy</u>, give the <u>correct units</u> where needed, and always <u>check your answer</u> is sensible.

2) **Show <u>each step</u> in your <u>working</u>.**
You're less likely to make a mistake if you write things out clearly and in stages. Even if your final answer's wrong, you might pick up a few method marks if you've shown all your working.

3) **Look at the number of <u>marks</u> a question is worth.**
If a question's worth 2 or more marks it's probably going to require you to do a few steps. Make sure you write down what you're doing at each stage.

4) **Give <u>exact</u> answers when the question asks you to.**
When you're asked for an <u>exact answer</u> you'll probably need to leave your answer in terms of π or as a fraction. <u>Don't round</u> at any stage in your calculation. If a <u>trigonometry</u> question asks you for an exact answer, it's a big hint that you're going to have to use values of <u>common angles</u>.

These handy hints might help you pick up a couple of extra marks — but they're no use if you haven't learnt the stuff in the first place. So make sure you revise well and do as many practice questions as you can.

5) **Learn the <u>formulas</u>.**
Most of the formulas you'll need in your exams <u>won't</u> be given to you, so <u>learn them</u>.

Using Your Calculator

1) Before your exam, clear the memory of your calculator and check that it's in <u>degrees mode</u>. This is important for any <u>trigonometry</u> questions.

2) If you're working out a <u>big calculation</u> on your calculator, it's best to do it in <u>stages</u> and use the <u>memory</u> to store the answers to the different parts. If you try to do it all in one go, it's easy to mess it up.

3) If you're going to be a renegade and do a question all in one go on your calculator, use <u>brackets</u> so the calculator knows which bits to do first.

REMEMBER: <u>The 2nd Handy Hint</u> still applies, even if you're using a calculator — you should still write down <u>all</u> the steps you are doing so the examiner can see the method you're using.

LCM and HCF

1 $200 = 2^3 \times 5^2$ and $1750 = 2 \times 5^3 \times 7$

Write as a product of prime factors:

a)   the lowest common multiple of 200 and 1750,

....

[1]

b)   the highest common factor of 200 and 1750.

....

[1]

[Total 2 marks]

2 $M = 3^6 \times 5^3 \times 11^5$ and $N = 3^4 \times 5^7 \times 11^6$.

Write as a product of prime factors:

a)   the LCM of M and N,

....

[1]

b)   the HCF of M and N.

....

[1]

[Total 2 marks]

3 $P = 2 \times 3^4 \times 5^3$ and $Q = 2^6 \times 3 \times 5^7$.

Write as a product of prime factors:

a)   the LCM of 12 and P,

....

[2]

b)   the HCF of 18 and Q.

....

[2]

[Total 4 marks]

4

4   Dan, Jess and Sufjan are exercising with skipping ropes.

Dan skips in sets of 12, Jess skips in sets of 24, and Sufjan skips in sets of 32.
They stop after they have all skipped the same number of times.

Find the smallest number of sets that each person could have completed.

Multiples of 12 are: 12, 24, ..., ..., ..., ..., ..., ..., ..., ...
Multiples of 24 are: 24, 48, ..., ..., ..., ..., ...
Multiples of 32 are: 32, 64, ..., ..., ...

The LCM of 12, 24 and 32 is ...., which is the smallest number of skips they need to complete.
The smallest number of sets Dan needs to complete is: .... ÷ .... = ... sets
The smallest number of sets Jess needs to complete is: .... ÷ .... = ... sets
The smallest number of sets Sufjan needs to complete is: .... ÷ .... = ... sets

Dan: .... sets   Jess: .... sets   Sufjan: .... sets

[Total 3 marks]

5   Kelly is posting cards to advertise the opening of her shop.

She can buy envelopes in packs of 18, stamps in packs of 20, and cards in packs of 36.
Each advertisement needs one of each item. She doesn't want to have any items left over.

What is the smallest number of packs of each item that Kelly could buy?

.... packs of envelopes   .... packs of cards   .... packs of stamps

[Total 3 marks]

6   Ami is making sandwiches.

She has 42 cheese slices, 63 apple slices and 84 tomato slices.
She makes as many identical sandwiches as possible without any ingredients left over.

How many slices of each ingredient does Ami put in each sandwich?

First, find the number of sandwiches she makes.

.... cheese slices   .... apple slices   .... tomato slices

[Total 3 marks]

Score:

17

Fractions

1 Work out $\frac{7}{9}$ of $7\frac{7}{8}$. Give your answer as a mixed number its simplest form.

....

[Total 2 marks]

2 Which of the fractions $\frac{5}{6}$ or $\frac{11}{9}$ is closer to 1?

....

[Total 3 marks]

3 Marla has chickens. $\frac{5}{7}$ of her chickens lay an egg and $\frac{8}{15}$ of the eggs are brown.

What fraction of her chickens laid an egg that is not brown?
Give your answer in its simplest form.

....

[Total 3 marks]

4 Owen and his friends split into two equal teams to play rugby.
$\frac{2}{3}$ of one team and $\frac{4}{5}$ of the other team are wearing black boots.

What fraction of all the rugby players are wearing black boots?

....

[Total 3 marks]

6

5 Aftab's book collection is split equally onto three full shelves. $\frac{2}{5}$ of the first shelf and $\frac{1}{4}$ of the second shelf are poetry books. There are no poetry books on the third shelf.

What fraction of his book collection is made up of poetry books?

....

[Total 3 marks]

6 Sarah performed at 70 parties last year. She worked as a balloon artist for $\frac{3}{14}$ of the parties, as a clown for $\frac{5}{14}$ of the parties, and as a magician for the remaining parties.

She was paid £90 for each balloon party, £96 for each clown party and £100 for each magic party.

What fraction of Sarah's total income came from magic parties?
Give your answer in its simplest form.

....

[Total 4 marks]

7 A shop sells jeans in different styles: $\frac{1}{3}$ are regular, $\frac{4}{7}$ are skinny and the rest are baggy. $\frac{3}{4}$ of the jeans in all three styles are coloured blue.

There are 42 pairs of regular blue jeans. How many pairs of baggy blue jeans are there?

$\dfrac{\text{............}}{\text{............}} \times \dfrac{\text{............}}{\text{............}} = \dfrac{\text{............}}{\text{............}}$ of the jeans are regular and blue.

Total number of pairs of jeans = ... $\div \dfrac{\text{............}}{\text{............}}$ = ...

$1 - \dfrac{\text{............}}{\text{............}} - \dfrac{\text{............}}{\text{............}} = \dfrac{\text{............}}{\text{............}}$ of the jeans are baggy.

$\dfrac{\text{............}}{\text{............}} \times \dfrac{\text{............}}{\text{............}} = \dfrac{\text{............}}{\text{............}}$ of the jeans are baggy and blue.

So number of pairs of baggy blue jeans = ... $\times \dfrac{\text{............}}{\text{............}}$ = ...

....

[Total 5 marks]

Score: ☐

23

Section One — Number

Rounding Errors

1 Sanya says, "I'm 160 cm tall to two significant figures."

What is the minimum height that she could be?

.... cm

[Total 1 mark]

2 Kamal has a bucket of popcorn. Its mass is 216 g to the nearest gram.

What are the minimum and maximum possible masses of the popcorn?

Minimum mass: .... g

Maximum mass: .... g

[Total 2 marks]

3 Laura has £38 to spend. Her shopping costs £35 to the nearest pound.

She wants to pay for her shopping and then buy a £2.50 bus ticket.
Can she definitely do this? Explain your answer.

....

....

[Total 2 marks]

4 Write down the error interval for these rounded numbers.

a) $x = 6.4$ to one decimal place

Smallest possible value of x = 6.4 − .... = ...

Largest possible value of x = 6.4 + ... = ...

So the error interval is: .... ≤ x < ....

....

[2]

b) $y = 7.20$ to two decimal places

....

[2]

[Total 4 marks]

5 Amna finished a race in a time of T seconds.

a) A timer recorded T to be 24.7 seconds, correct to one decimal place.
Write down the error interval for this time.

....

[2]

b) A second timer recorded T to be 24.65 seconds, correct to two decimal places.
Write down an interval to show the range of values of T that are a now possible.

....

[2]

[Total 4 marks]

6 George counts the number of cars in four car parks separately. By rounding each number to the nearest ten, he estimates that there are 110 cars in total.

What is the minimum possible total number of cars?

> You don't need to find what each of the four numbers are — only how much smaller they could be.

.... cars

[Total 2 marks]

7 An equilateral triangle has side lengths of 5 cm to the nearest centimetre.

a) Write down the error interval for the side lengths, L, of the triangle.

....

[2]

b) Write down the error interval for the perimeter, P, of the triangle.

....

[2]

[Total 4 marks]

Exam Practice Tip

If you're asked a tricky question on using error intervals, it's a good idea to think about what happens when you use the maximum or minimum values in the calculation. If that works, great! But remember to read the question carefully — there may be extra information that rules out certain numbers being the answer.

Score

[ ]

19

Powers

1 Simplify these expressions. Leave your answer in index form.

a) $\dfrac{5^2 \times 5^4}{5^3}$

....
[1]

b) $(7^6)^3 \div 7^3$

....
[1]

[Total 2 marks]

2 Find the exact value of:

a) 3^{-2}

....
[1]

b) $2^{-4} \times 2^7$

....
[1]

c) $7^{-3} \div 7^{-5}$

....
[1]

[Total 3 marks]

3 Calculate the value of these expressions.

a) $4^7 \times (4^3 \times 4^2)^{-1}$

....
[2]

b) $(2^{-2} \times 2^{-3}) \div 2^{-9}$

....
[2]

[Total 4 marks]

Score: ☐

9

 ☐   ☐   ☐

Standard Form

1 Answer each question below.

a) Write 5.28×10^5 as an ordinary number.

....

[1]

b) Write 0.0009762 in standard form.

....

[1]

c) Work out $\dfrac{(7 \times 10^3) \times (3 \times 10^{-5})}{2.5 \times 10^2}$.

....

[2]

[Total 4 marks]

2 Work out these calculations.

Give your answers in standard form.

a) $(3 \times 10^2) \times (4 \times 10^3)$

....

[2]

b) $(8 \times 10^7) \div (2 \times 10^4)$

....

[2]

[Total 4 marks]

3 An hourglass contains 2.3×10^4 grains of sand.
One grain of sand weighs approximately 4×10^{-3} g.

What is the total weight of the sand in the hourglass?
Give your answer as an ordinary number.

.... g

[Total 2 marks]

4 Work out the following.

Give your answers in standard form.

a) $(5.2 \times 10^6) + (6.4 \times 10^5)$

....

[2]

b) $(9.7 \times 10^{-2}) - (8 \times 10^{-3})$

....

[2]

[Total 4 marks]

5 The table below shows the diameter of some planets.

Planet	Diameter (km)
Mercury	4.88×10^3
Earth	1.27×10^4
Saturn	1.16×10^5
Uranus	5.07×10^4

a) Which planet has the largest diameter?

....

[1]

b) How much larger is the diameter of Uranus than the diameter of Earth?
Give your answer as an ordinary number.

.... km

[2]

c) Jupiter has a diameter of 140 000 km. Is this smaller or larger than the
combined diameters of Mercury and Saturn? Explain your answer.

....

....

[3]

[Total 6 marks]

Score:

20

Surds

1   Simplify the following expressions.

 a) $2\sqrt{7} + 4 - \sqrt{7}$

....
[1]

     b) $-2\sqrt{3} + 1 + 4\sqrt{3} - 6$

....
[2]

[Total 3 marks]

2   Find the perimeter of this shape.

 Give your answer in its simplest form.

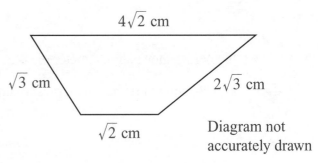

$4\sqrt{2}$ cm

$\sqrt{3}$ cm $2\sqrt{3}$ cm

$\sqrt{2}$ cm   Diagram not accurately drawn

.... cm
[Total 3 marks]

3 $P = \sqrt{5} - \sqrt{7}$ and $Q = \sqrt{5} - 2\sqrt{7}$.

 Find and simplify:
a) $P + Q$

....
[2]

     b) $Q - P$

....
[2]

[Total 4 marks]

Score: ☐

10

Expanding Brackets

1 Expand and simplify the following:

a) $(x + 7)(2x - 2)$

....

[2]

b) $(3x - 2)(x - 5)$

....

[2]

[Total 4 marks]

2 Expand and simplify the following:

a) $(3x + 1)^2$

....

[2]

b) $(4x - 2)^2$

....

[2]

[Total 4 marks]

3 A square has side length $(2x + 7)$ cm.

Write an expression for the area of the square.
Give your answer in the form $ax^2 + bx + c$, where a, b and c are integers.

$(2x + 7)$ cm

.... cm^2

[Total 3 marks]

Score:

11

Factorising

1 Fully factorise each of the following expressions.

a) $5x^2 - 35x$

$5x^2 - 35x = 5(\text{..................} - \text{...................})$

$= 5\text{.........}(\text{..................} - \text{...................})$

....

[2]

b) $6y + 3xy$

....

[2]

c) $xy^2 - x^2y$

....

[2]

[Total 6 marks]

2 Factorise the following expressions.

a) $x^2 - 36$

....

[2]

b) $49y^2 - 1$

....

[2]

c) $16r^2 - 81s^2$

....

[2]

[Total 6 marks]

Exam Practice Tip

Difference of two squares questions can sometimes be difficult to spot, which can lead to you trying other factorising techniques that will be much trickier to use. So whenever you are looking to factorise an expression, always check to see if one squared term is being subtracted from another squared term.

Score

12

Solving Equations

1 Find the solution to each of the following equations.

a) $6(x-2) = -3(x-5)$

$x = $ ....
[3]

b) $4(3y-2) = 2(2y-3)$

$y = $ ....
[3]

[Total 6 marks]

2 Solve the following equations:

a) $a^2 = 49$

$a = $ ....
[2]

b) $4b^2 = 64$

$b = $ ....
[2]

c) $c^2 + 19 = 100$

$c = $ ....
[2]

[Total 6 marks]

16

3 Solve the following equations:

a) $m^2 + 5 = (m - 2)(m + 5)$

$m^2 + 5 = m^2 +$ .... $-$ .... $-$ ....

$m^2 + 5 = m^2 +$ .... $-$ ....

.... $-$ .... $= 5$

.... $m =$ ...., so $m =$ ....

$m =$ ....

[3]

b) $(n + 3)(n + 2) = (n - 3)(n + 6)$

$n =$ ....

[4]

[Total 7 marks]

4 Find the solution to each of the following equations.

a) $\dfrac{2r - 5}{3} = \dfrac{r + 1}{5}$

$r =$ ....

[4]

b) $\dfrac{s - 9}{5} = \sqrt[3]{2s^3 + 6s^3}$

$s =$ ....

[4]

[Total 8 marks]

Score: ⬚

27

Equations from Words and Diagrams

1 Han, Claire and Kate each think of a number. Claire's number is a third of Han's number. Kate's number is eight more than Claire's number. The three numbers sum to 88.

What number is Claire thinking of?

Call Claire's number x.

Then Han's number is .... and Kate's number is .... + ...

The numbers sum to 88, so .... + ... + (................. + ...) = 88

.... + ... = 88, so .... = ... and x = ...

So the number Claire is thinking of is ....

....

[Total 3 marks]

2 Triangle *ABC* below has a perimeter of 21 cm. Side *BC* is twice as long as *AB*.

Find the length of *BC*.

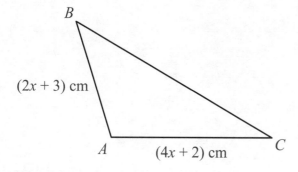

$(2x + 3)$ cm

$(4x + 2)$ cm

.... cm
[Total 4 marks]

3 Caitlin, Adam and Maya play a game of cards. Caitlin scores four times as many points as Adam. Adam scores twelve more points than Maya. They score 78 points altogether.

How many points does each player score?

Caitlin: ...., Adam: ...., Maya: ....
[Total 4 marks]

4 Three friends are comparing the cost of their shopping.
Lacey spent 4 times as much as Jin and Jin spent £5 more than Leon.
The difference between Lacey and Jin's amount is £30.

How much did they spend in total?

£ ....

[Total 3 marks]

5 The perimeter of the regular pentagon below is double the perimeter of the rectangle.

Find the side length of the pentagon.

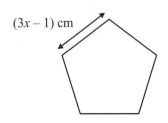

(3x – 1) cm

2x cm

(x + 4) cm

.... cm

[Total 4 marks]

6 Three numbers multiply together to give 18. The middle number is double the smallest number. The largest number is 3 times the sum of the other two numbers.

What are the three numbers?

.... , ... , ...

[Total 4 marks]

Score:

22

Rearranging Formulas

1   Rearrange the formula $a - 4 = \dfrac{b-1}{5}$ to make b the subject.

....

[Total 2 marks]

2   The formula for the kinetic energy (K) of an object is $K = \dfrac{mv^2}{2}$,
    where m is mass of the object and v is the velocity of the object.

    Rearrange the formula to find a formula for the velocity of the object.

....

[Total 3 marks]

3   Rearrange the formula $r = s^2 - (t + 2)^2$ to make t the subject.

....

[Total 3 marks]

4   Rearrange the formula $m = \dfrac{1}{n-2} + 7$ to make n the subject.

....

[Total 3 marks]

Score:

11

Sequences

1 A sequence starts 1, 4, 16, 64, ...

a) Describe the term-to-term rule for the sequence.

....

[1]

b) Circle the correct description of the sequence.

arithmetic   geometric   quadratic   square numbers

[1]

[Total 2 marks]

2 The first four terms of a sequence are 5, 13, 21, 29.

a) Find the nth term of the sequence.

....

[2]

b) Maddy claims that 52 is a term in the sequence.
Is she correct? Explain your answer.

....

....

[2]

c) Find the first number in the sequence that is greater than 500.

....

[3]

[Total 7 marks]

3 The 5th and 6th terms of a Fibonacci-type sequence are 18 and 29.

Each term in the sequence is the sum of the previous two terms.
a)   Find the 7th and 8th terms in the sequence.

.... and ....
[2]

b)   Find the 3rd and 4th terms in the sequence.

.... and ....
[2]

[Total 4 marks]

4 The first four terms of a quadratic sequence are 2, 11, 26, 47.

a)   Show that the next odd term in the sequence is 107.

[2]

b)   The *n*th term for this sequence is $3n^2 - 1$.
     Given that 506 is in the sequence, what is its position?

....
[3]

[Total 7 marks]

Score:

20

Inequalities

1 Solve the following inequalities.

a) $6a < 78$

....

[1]

b) $3b + 4 \geq 54 - 2b$

....

[2]

b) $2c - 4 \leq 5c + 17$

....

[2]

[Total 5 marks]

2 Kaya thinks of a positive integer that satisfies the inequality $\dfrac{11 - 2x}{3} \geq x - 3$.

a) Solve the inequality.

....

[3]

b) Write down the possible numbers that Kaya could be thinking of.

....

[1]

[Total 4 marks]

3 A regular hexagon has sides of length $(3x + 1)$ cm.
The perimeter of the hexagon is less than or equal to 114 cm.

a) Write an inequality using x to describe the perimeter of the hexagon.
Give your answer in the form $ax + b \leq c$, where a, b and c are integers.

....

[2]

b) Given that $x > 5$, find the side length of the hexagon.

.... cm

[3]

[Total 5 marks]

4 Grace and Salim are cycling laps around a park. Each lap has a length of x km.

- Grace completes 9 laps.
- Salim completes 7 laps, plus an additional 10 km.

a) Circle the inequality below that shows Salim cycled further than Grace.

$7x + 10 \geq 9x$ $\qquad$ $9x > 7x + 10$ $\qquad$ $7x > 9x + 10$ $\qquad$ $7x + 10 > 9x$

[1]

b) (i) Solve the inequality you chose for part a).

....

[2]

(ii) x is a whole number. What is the furthest that Salim could have cycled?

.... km

[2]

[Total 5 marks]

Score:

19

Quadratic Equations

1 Fully factorise the expression $x^2 + 8x + 7$.

....

[Total 2 marks]

2 Fully factorise the expression $x^2 - 5x + 4$.

$x^2 - 5x + 4 = (x - \text{.................})(x - \text{.................})$

....

[Total 2 marks]

3 $(x + 6)(x - 1) = 0$ is a fully factorised quadratic equation.

Sammy claims the solutions to the equation are 6 and –1.
Is he correct? Explain your answer.

....

....

....

[Total 2 marks]

4 Look at the following quadratic equation: $x^2 - x - 2 = 0$.

a) Fully factorise the expression $x^2 - x - 2$.

....

[2]

b) Use your answer to part a) to solve the equation $x^2 - x - 2 = 0$.

$x = \text{.................}$ or $x = \text{.................}$

[1]

[Total 3 marks]

5 Solve the equation $x^2 + 7x + 10 = 0$.

....

[Total 3 marks]

6 Solve the equation $x^2 - x = 42$.

....

[Total 4 marks]

7 A diagram of a rectangle is shown on the right.

$(x + 2)$ cm

a) Find an expression for the area of the rectangle.
    Give your answer in the form $x^2 + ax + b$.

$(x - 3)$ cm

.... cm²

[2]

b) The area of the rectangle is 24 cm².
    Given that x is positive, find the value of x.

> Make sure your quadratic equals zero before factorising.

$x =$ ....

[5]

[Total 7 marks]

Score:

23

Section Two — Algebra

Simultaneous Equations

1   Solve this pair of simultaneous equations.

$5x + 3y = 14$
$2x + 3y = 11$

$x = \text{...............}$ $y = \text{...............}$
[Total 2 marks]

2   Solve this pair of simultaneous equations.

$2x + 4y = 12$
$4x + 5y = 18$

$x = \text{...............}$ $y = \text{...............}$
[Total 3 marks]

3   Solve this pair of simultaneous equations.

$3x - 8y = 7$
$2x - 2y = 8$

$x = \text{...............}$ $y = \text{...............}$
[Total 3 marks]

4   Solve this pair of simultaneous equations.

$2x + 3y = 16$
$3x + 2y = 14$

$x = \text{...............}$ $y = \text{...............}$
[Total 4 marks]

5 Solve this pair of simultaneous equations.

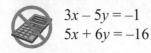

$3x - 5y = -1$
$5x + 6y = -16$

$x =$ .... $y =$ ....
[Total 4 marks]

6 Amar is *x* years old and Carla is *y* years old.
The difference between their ages is 8 and the sum of their ages is 56.

If Carla is older than Amar, how old are they both?

Difference between ages is 8, so .... – .... = ...

Sum of ages is 56, so .... + ... = ...

Amar: ....   Carla: ....
[Total 4 marks]

7 In a card game you score *x* points for playing a spade and *y* points for playing a diamond.

- Linus plays 4 spades and 1 diamonds, which scores him 17 points.
- Selma plays 2 spades and 3 diamonds, which scores her 21 points.

How many points are a spade and a diamond each worth?

Spade: ....   Diamond: ....
[Total 5 marks]

Score:
25

Proof

1 For each statement below, write down an example to show that the statement is incorrect.

a) The product of two square numbers is a multiple of 4.

....

[1]

b) The difference of two numbers is less than their sum.

....

[1]

[Total 2 marks]

2 Prove that $(n + 5)(2n - 4) + 2 \equiv 2(n^2 + 3n - 9)$.

[Total 3 marks]

3 r is a whole number. Show that $4(2r + 3) + 7(r - 1)$ is a multiple of 5.

[Total 3 marks]

4 Prove that $x(5x + 2) + 2(3x + 8) - 4x^2 = (x + 4)^2$ for all values of x.

[Total 3 marks]

5   Kara claims that if you double the length and width of a rectangle, then the new area is four times larger than the original area.

Show that Kara is correct.
Use x and y for length and width, as shown in the diagram.

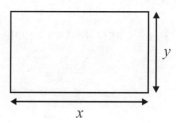

[Total 3 marks]

6   Prove that the sum of three consecutive integers is a multiple of 3.

[Total 4 marks]

7   Show there are values a and b that make the identity below true.

$2(ax + 2) - 3b + 4ax \equiv 18x + 1$

LHS: .... + ... − .... + ... = ...x + (.............)

If identity is true, then .... + ... = ... + ...

Compare x coefficients: .... = ..., so a = ...

Compare constants: .... = ..., so b = ...

[Total 5 marks]

Exam Practice Tip

I admit it, these proof questions can definitely be tricky, but as you do more questions you'll pick up some hints and tips that can help you solve the different types. For example, if you're proving something is a multiple of a number, then you know at some point you need to factor that number out of the expression.

Score

23

Parallel Lines

1   Circle the **two** equations below whose graphs are parallel lines.

$$y = -2x \qquad\qquad 3y = 6x + 12 \qquad\qquad y = 2x^2 \qquad\qquad y = 2x - 2$$

Explain your answer.

....

....

[Total 3 marks]

2 $y = 7x - 5$ is the equation of a straight line.

Find the equation of the line parallel to $y = 7x - 5$ which passes through:

a)   the origin,

....

[1]

b)   the point $(1, 6)$. $y = mx + c = \text{...........} x + c$

                      When $x = \text{..........}$, $y = \text{..........}$

                      so $\text{..........} = (\text{..........} \times \text{..........}) + c$

                            $c = \text{..........}$

                      So $y = \text{...}$

....

[3]

[Total 4 marks]

3   Line **L** is plotted on the grid below.

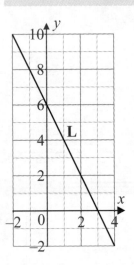

Find the *y*-intercept of the line parallel to **L** that passes through $(-3, 7)$.

....

[Total 3 marks]

4 $2y + 8x = 4$ and $8x - 2y = 4$ are equations of straight lines.

Show that these lines are **not** parallel. Do not use a graphical method.

[Total 3 marks]

5 $2x - 3y - 4 = 0$ is the equation of a straight line.

Find the equation of the line parallel to $2x - 3y - 4 = 0$ which passes through the point (6, 1).

....

[Total 4 marks]

6 Line **M** has the equation $y + 3x = 3$.

Line **N** is parallel to **M** and has the equation $3y - Ax = 3$ for some number A.

a) Find the value of A.

Compare the equations in $y = mx + c$ form.

$A = $ ....
[3]

b) Joe plots the graphs of both lines on a standard coordinate grid.
He says, "The line **M** lies below the line **N**."

Is he correct? Explain your answer.

....

....

[1]

[Total 4 marks]

Score: ☐

21

Section Three — Graphs

Straight-Line Graphs

1   Kevin has sketched a graph of the line **L** through points A (0, –2) and B (4, 6).

Find the equation of the line.

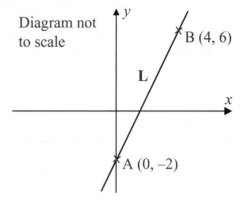

Diagram not to scale

Gradient = $\dfrac{\text{change in } y}{\text{change in } x}$ = $\dfrac{\text{............} - \text{............}}{\text{............} - \text{............}}$ = $\dfrac{\text{............}}{\text{............}}$ = ...

So y = ... x + c

Use A to find c: when x = ..., y = ...

.... = (............ × ....) + c

c = ...

So y = ...

....

[Total 4 marks]

2   A straight line passes through the points (1, 4) and (2, 1).

Find the equation of the line.

....

[Total 4 marks]

3   A straight line has an *x*-intercept at *x* = –3 and passes through the point (5, 4).

a)   Find the equation of the line.

....

[4]

b)   Does the point (–1, 2) lie above, below or on the line?
     Explain your answer.

....

....

[1]

[Total 5 marks]

Section Three — Graphs

4 Leandra has drawn a square *ABCD* on a coordinate grid, shown below.

a) Write down the coordinates of *A* and *C*.

A: (........., ...)   C: (........., ...)

[2]

b) Find the equation of the straight line that passes through *A* and *C*.

D (–6, 4)   *C*

A   *B* (2, –4)

Diagram not to scale

....

[4]

c) Which of the triangles *ABC* or *ACD* contains the point (0, 1)? Explain your answer.

....

....

[1]

[Total 7 marks]

5 Points P (1, 5), Q (1, 1) and R (3, 5) are sketched on the diagram below.

M is the midpoint of the line segment QR.

a) Write down the coordinates of M.

(........., ...)

[2]

b) Find the equation of the straight line that passes through P and M.

P

×R

×M

×Q

Diagram not to scale

....

[4]

[Total 6 marks]

Score:

26

Section Three — Graphs

Quadratic Graphs

1   The graph of $y = x^2 - 10x + 27$ is shown on the right.

Write down the coordinates of the turning point of the graph.

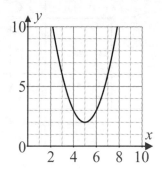

(............., ...)
[Total 1 mark]

2   A table of values for $y = -x^2 + 2x + 1$ is shown below.

x	−1	0	1	2	3
y		1	2		

a)   Complete the table of values.

[2]

b)   Plot the points from the table and draw the graph of $y = -x^2 + 2x + 1$ on the grid to the right.

[2]

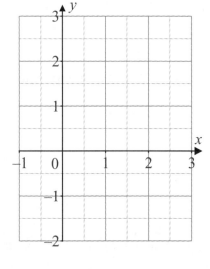

c)   Write down the coordinates of the turning point of the graph.

(..............., ...)
[1]

[Total 5 marks]

3   The graph of $y = x^2 + x - 2$ is drawn on the grid below.

Find the coordinates of the turning point of the graph.

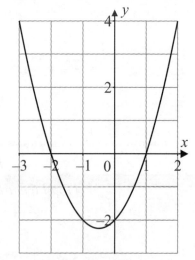

The graph has the same y-value at x = ... and x = ...

The x-coordinate of the turning point is halfway

between these two values: x = $\dfrac{............. + ...}{2}$ = ...

And the y-coordinate of the turning point is:

y = (.............)² + ... − 2

= ....

(..............., ...)
[Total 4 marks]

4 A table of values for $y = x^2 - 5x + 4$ is shown below.

x	0	1	2	3	4	5
y	4	0				

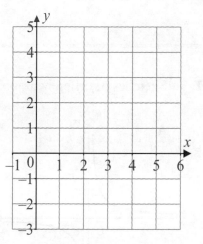

a) Complete the table above.

[2]

b) Plot the points from the table and draw the graph of $y = x^2 - 5x + 4$ on the grid to the right.

[2]

c) Find the coordinates of the turning point of the graph.

(................, ...)

[4]

[Total 8 marks]

5 A table of values for $y = 1 - 3x - x^2$ is shown below.

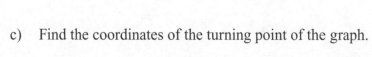

x	−3	−2	−1	0	1
y				1	

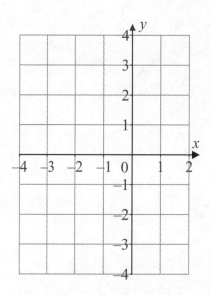

a) Complete the table above.

[2]

b) Plot the points from the table and draw the graph of $y = 1 - 3x - x^2$ on the grid to the right.

[2]

c) Find the coordinates of the turning point of the graph.

(................, ...)

[4]

[Total 8 marks]

Exam Practice Tip

The sign on the x^2 term tells you the shape of a quadratic graph — positive means the graph is u-shaped, and negative means the graph is n-shaped. If the turning point isn't on a point where two grid lines meet, then you'll have to work it out yourself. Afterwards, check the graph to see if your answer looks sensible.

Score

26

Harder Graphs

1   Sketches of different graphs are shown below.

A
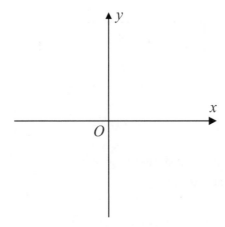
B
C

Write down the letter of the graph which shows $y = x^3$.

....

[Total 1 mark]

2   Sketch the graphs of the following equations.
     Label any points where they intersect the axes.

a) $y = \dfrac{1}{x}$

[2]

b) $y = -x^3$

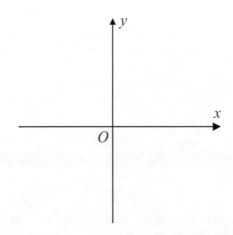

[2]

[Total 4 marks]

3 Lindsay has sketched the graph of one of the equations below. She has labelled the point where it crosses the y-axis.

Circle the equation of this graph.

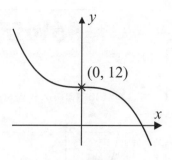

$y = x^3 + 12$ $y = -x^3 - 12$ $y = x^3 - 12$ $y = -x^3 + 12$

[Total 1 mark]

4 A table of values for $y = x^3 + 4$ is shown below.

x	−2	−1	0	1	2
y			4	5	

a) Complete the table above.

[2]

b) Plot the points from the table and draw the graph of $y = x^3 + 4$ on the grid to the right.

[2]

[Total 4 marks]

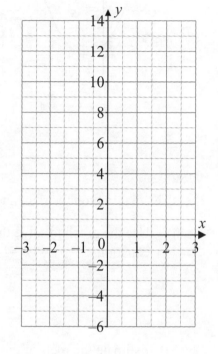

5 A table of values for $y = x^3 - 7$ is shown below.

x	−2	−1	0	1	2
y				−6	1

a) Complete the table above.

[2]

b) Plot the points from the table and draw the graph of $y = x^3 - 7$ on the grid to the right.

[2]

[Total 4 marks]

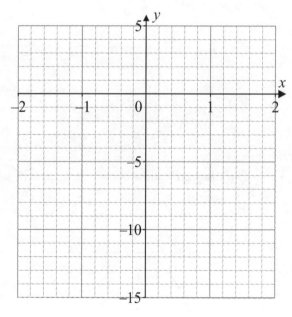

Score:

14

Section Three — Graphs

Solving Quadratics Using Graphs

1 The diagram below shows the graph of $y = x^2 - x - 2$.

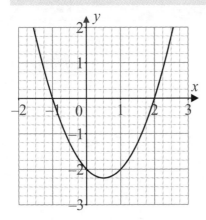

a) Find the roots of $x^2 - x - 2 = 0$ using the graph.

....

[1]

b) Use the graph to solve the equation $x^2 - x - 2 = -2$.

The x-values where the curve crosses the line y = –2

are x = ... and x = ...

....

[1]

[Total 2 marks]

2 The diagram on the right shows the graph of $y = x^2 - 3x - 12$.

a) Use the graph to solve the
equation $x^2 - 3x - 12 = -8$.

....

[1]

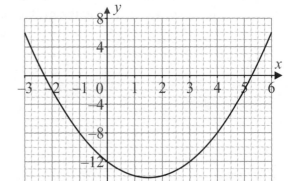

b) Estimate the roots of the equation
$x^2 - 3x - 12 = 0$ using the graph.

....

[2]

[Total 3 marks]

3 The diagram below shows the graph of $y = a + 6x - 3x^2$.

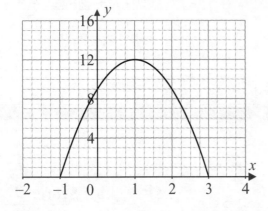

a) Circle the value of a.

    –1   0   3   9   12

[1]

b) Use the graph to find approximate solutions
to the equation $a + 6x - 3x^2 = 5$.

....

[2]

[Total 3 marks]

4 Dani has started to draw the graph of $y = x^2 - 2x - 4$ on the grid below.

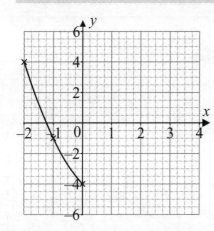

a) Complete her table of values:

x	−2	−1	0	1	2	3	4
y	4	−1	−4				

[2]

b) Complete the graph of $y = x^2 - 2x - 4$ on the grid.

[2]

c) Use the graph to estimate the solutions of $x^2 - 2x - 4 = 1$.

....

[2]

[Total 6 marks]

5 Kofi has drawn the graph of $y = x^2$ on the grid to the right.

He says, "The graph shows that $\sqrt{8} = 3$ to the nearest whole number."
Is he correct? Explain your answer.

Think about how squares
and square-roots are related.

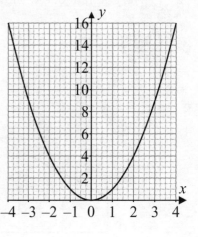

....

....

[Total 2 marks]

6 The diagram below shows the graph of $y = x^2 + 6x + 13$.

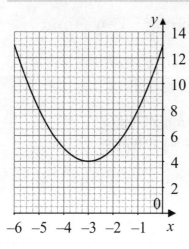

Find the value of c for which the equation $x^2 + 6x + 13 = c$ has:

a) solutions $x = -5$ and $x = -1$,

$c =$ ....

[2]

b) exactly one solution.

$c =$ ....

[2]

[Total 4 marks]

Score:

20

Simultaneous Equations and Graphs

1   Use the graphs on the right to solve these simultaneous equations.

a) $2y = 5x - 9$
       $3y = 2x + 3$

$x =$ .... $y =$ ....

[1]

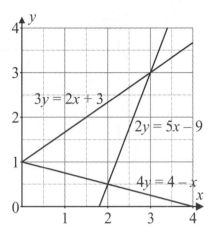

b) $2y = 5x - 9$
       $4y = 4 - x$

$x =$ .... $y =$ ....

[1]

[Total 2 marks]

2   The diagram below shows the graph of $2y = x - 1$.

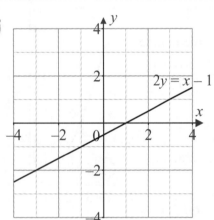

a)   Draw the graph of $y = 2x + 1$ on the same grid.

[2]

b)   Use the graphs to solve the simultaneous equations:
       $2y = x - 1$
       $y = 2x + 1$

$x =$ .... $y =$ ....

[1]

[Total 3 marks]

3   The diagram below shows the graphs of $y = 2x + 3$ and $y = 6 - 4x$.

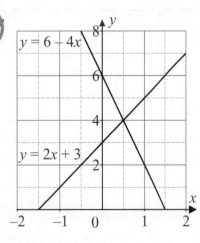

a)   Use the diagram to solve $2x + 3 = 6 - 4x$.

$x =$ ....

[1]

b)   By drawing another straight line,
      solve these simultaneous equations:
       $y = 6 - 4x$
       $y = x + 1$

$x =$ .... $y =$ ....

[3]

[Total 4 marks]

Section Three — Graphs

4 Sofia has drawn the graphs of $2y - x = 4$ and $8y + 7x = 28$ on the grid below.

She wants to solve these simultaneous equations:
$$2y - x = 4$$
$$8y + 7x = 28$$

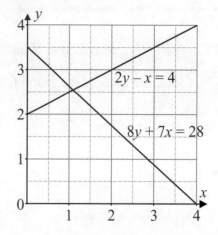

a) Explain why Sofia **cannot** use her graphs to find an exact solution to the simultaneous equations.

....

....

....

[1]

b) Find an approximate solution to the simultaneous equations.

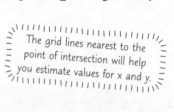

The grid lines nearest to the point of intersection will help you estimate values for x and y.

$x =$ .... $y =$ ....

[1]

[Total 2 marks]

5 The diagram below shows the graph of $5y = 7 - 5x$.

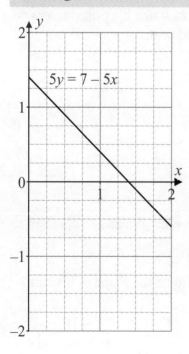

By drawing another straight line, find an approximate solution to the simultaneous equations:
$$5y = 7 - 5x$$
$$y = 2x - 3$$

$x =$ .... $y =$ ....

[Total 3 marks]

Exam Practice Tip

Draw your lines straight and thin to get the most accurate estimates. So use a sharp pencil (not a chunky felt tip), a straight ruler (not a wavy one) and a steady hand. You can still check approximate solutions by putting the numbers back into the equations — the two sides won't be equal but they should be fairly close.

Score

14

Real-Life Graphs

1   A painting increases in value by the same amount each year.

Circle the letter of the graph that shows this.

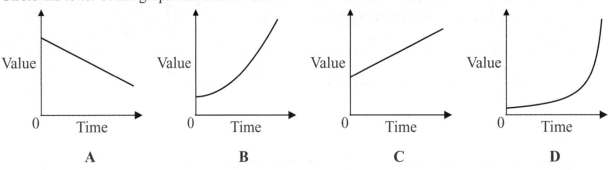

A   **B**   **C**   **D**

[Total 1 mark]

2   Michelle uses the graph below to calculate the cost of sending a parcel.

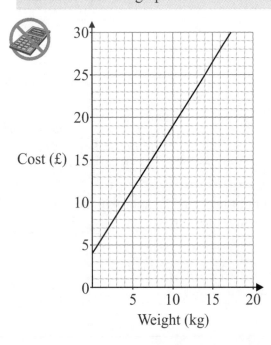

There is a fixed charge plus an amount depending on the weight of the parcel.

a)   Use the graph to estimate the cost of sending a 9 kg parcel.

£ ....
[2]

b)   Work out the rate at which the price increases, excluding the fixed cost.

£ .... per kg
[2]

[Total 4 marks]

3   Liam fills his sink with water. He then removes the plug and the water drains at a constant rate.

The graph below shows how the height of the water changes.

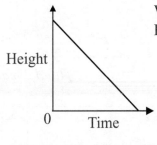

Which one of the following diagrams could be the shape of his sink?
Explain your answer.

A   **B**   **C**   **D**

....

....

[Total 1 mark]

4 Dinesh uses the formula $n = \dfrac{24}{t}$ to calculate the number of workers, n, that are needed to complete a task in a time of t hours.

a) He has started to draw the graph of $n = \dfrac{24}{t}$ on the grid below.

Complete the graph for values of t from 1 to 4.

Plot the points for t = 1 to 3 and draw a smooth curve.

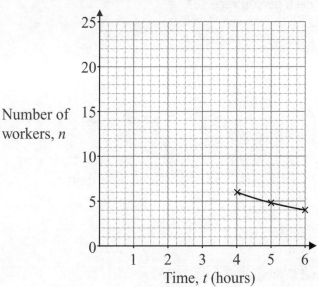

Number of workers, n

Time, t (hours)

[2]

b) Use the graph to estimate the time that 19 workers would take to complete the task.

.... hours and .... minutes

[2]

c) Dinesh wants to complete the task in less than $2\frac{1}{2}$ hours.
Use the graph to decide whether 9 workers can do this. Explain your answer.

....

....

[2]

d) Each worker is paid £11 per hour.
Dinesh says, "The total cost is the same whether I use 4 workers or 6 workers."
Is he correct? Show your working.

....

....

[3]

[Total 9 marks]

Exam Practice Tip

There's no telling exactly which real-life graphs you're going to see in your exams, but you can be prepared to tackle them all by knowing their common features. For example, the gradient always shows the rate of change — the steepness and direction of the graph shows how fast something is increasing and decreasing.

Score

15

Ratios

1   Sarah, Elliot and Kai share 45 grapes in the ratio $3:4:8$.

How many grapes will each person receive?

Sarah: ...., Elliot: ...., Kai: ....

[Total 3 marks]

2   The areas of rectangles A, B and C are in the ratio $2:7:3$.
The total area of all three rectangles is 96 cm^2.

Rectangle B has a width of 4 cm. Find the length of rectangle B.

.... cm

[Total 3 marks]

3   A seasoning is made by mixing garlic powder and salt in the ratio $3:8$.
Abby has 36 g of garlic powder and 90 g of salt.

What is the largest amount of the seasoning that she could make?

.... g

[Total 3 marks]

4 Logan played 10 games of badminton. His ratio of wins to losses was 3:2.
When Gina played badminton, her ratio of wins to losses was 1:3.

Gina won the same number of games as Logan. How many games did she play?

.... games
[Total 4 marks]

5 Hazel, Rabia and Callum share the winnings from a competition
in the ratio 3:5:2. Rabia receives £225 more than Callum.

How much did each person receive?

Hazel: £....................., Rabia: £....................., Callum: £.....................
[Total 4 marks]

6 A fruit salad contains bananas, apples and strawberries in the ratio 5:4:3.
Bananas cost £0.70 per kg, apples cost £3.10 per kg and strawberries cost £10 per kg.

What is the cost of the fruit needed to make 18 kg of fruit salad?

£.....................
[Total 5 marks]

Score:

22

Direct and Inverse Proportion

1   The soup recipe shown below will make 15 portions.

Spicy Soup
720 g carrots
540 g parsnips
0.9 kg potatoes
5 chillies

Clarence wants to make 27 portions of soup.
How much of each ingredient does he need?

Carrots: .... g

Parsnips: .... g

Potatoes: .... kg

Chillies: ....

[Total 3 marks]

2   Gary works at a car wash. He earns £9 for each car that he washes.

On Monday he:
•   washes 5 cars between 8:15 am and 12:00 pm,
•   takes a 45 minute lunch break,
•   then continues to wash cars until 5:15 pm.

How much did Gary earn from washing cars on Monday?
Assume he washes cars at a fixed rate.

£ ....

[Total 3 marks]

3 The amount of fuel used by a lawnmower (f ml) is directly proportional to the area (g m^2) of grass cut by the lawnmover. The lawnmower uses 240 ml of fuel to cut 75 m^2 of grass.

a) On the axes below, sketch a graph to show the relationship between f and g.
Mark at least two points on your graph.

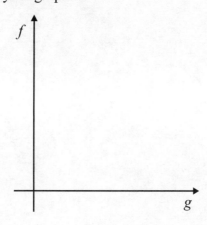

[3]

b) Write an equation in the form $f = Ag$ that represents this relationship.

....

[2]

[Total 5 marks]

4 The number of builders (b) working on a house is inversely proportional to the time (d days) it takes to build the house.

a) Circle the letter of the graph below that shows the relationship between b and d.

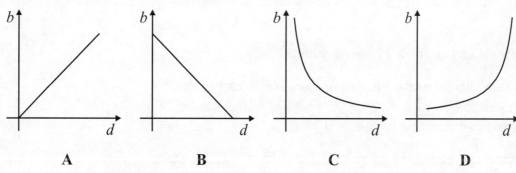

| A | B | C | D |

[1]

b) 8 builders take 170 days to build a house.
How many days would it take 5 builders to build a house?

.... days

[2]

[Total 3 marks]

Section Four — Ratio and Proportion

5 Fatima is planning a banquet. She wants the food to be served in under 45 minutes. She knows that 8 waiters would take 60 minutes to serve the food.

Find the smallest number of waiters that are needed, assuming the same rate of service.

.... waiters

[Total 3 marks]

6 *a* is inversely proportional to *m*.

a) Circle **two** equations below that could represent the relationship between *a* and *m*.

$$a = Km \qquad am = K \qquad \frac{1}{a} = \frac{K}{m} \qquad a = \frac{K}{m} \qquad \frac{a}{m} = K$$

[2]

b) Complete this table of values.

a		6	12
m	15	20	

[2]

[Total 4 marks]

7 8 people can assemble 12 cars in 9 hours.

How long would it take 3 people to assemble 16 cars in total?

1 person can assemble 12 cars in 9 × .... = ... hours

1 person can assemble 1 car in .... ÷ 12 = ... hours

3 people can assemble 1 car in .... ÷ .... = ... hours

3 people can assemble 16 cars in .... × .... = ... hours

.... hours

[Total 4 marks]

Exam Practice Tip

When answering proportion questions always check if the things in the question are directly proportional or inversely proportional. The easiest way to do this is by thinking about the context in real life — e.g. the more people on a job, the less time it will take, so number of people and job time are inversely proportional.

Score

[ ]

25

Percentages

1   A company sells notepads for £2.50 each.
They release a new notepad that costs 18% more.

a)   What is the price of the new notepad?

£ ....
[2]

b)   One day they sold 340 notepads. 85% of them were the new notepads.
How much money did the company make in sales from notepads that day?

£ ....
[3]

[Total 5 marks]

2   A cupcake stall sells each cupcake for £1.40.
35% of the stall's monthly profit is donated to charity.

One month, the costs of the stall were £650 in total.

a)   How much money would be donated to charity if 820 cupcakes were sold that month?

£ ....
[3]

b)   The stall actually donated £336 to charity. How many cupcakes were sold?

.... cupcakes
[3]

[Total 6 marks]

3 On Monday, a bakery sells 57 rolls for a total of £18.24. On Tuesday, the bakery decreases the price of a roll and sells 71 rolls for a total of £19.88.

Find out how much a single roll costs on both days first.

Calculate the percentage decrease in the price of a roll.

.... %

[Total 3 marks]

4 At a football match, 90% of the fans are home fans and the rest are away fans. 80% of the home fans and 85% of the away fans are wearing their team's shirt.

What percentage of all the fans are **not** wearing their team's shirt?

.... %

[Total 4 marks]

5 176 singers enter the first round of a talent competition. The remaining entrants are dancers and musicians in the ratio 1 : 3.

35% of the competitors are knocked out, leaving 260 competitors in the second round.

What percentage of the competitors in the first round were musicians?

.... %

[Total 4 marks]

Score:

22

Compound Growth and Decay

1   Luca opens a savings account with a starting balance of £2400.
The bank pays 2% compound interest per annum.

    a)   How much money will be in the account after 4 years?
Give your answer to the nearest penny.

£.....................

[3]

    b)   How many years will it be before Luca has £2700 in his account?

.... years

[2]

[Total 5 marks]

2   The number of insects in a tank increases at a rate of 10%
each week. After 2 weeks there are 121 insects in the tank.

    a)   How many insects were in the tank at the start?

Using the formula, ... = Insects at start × (.................)⁻⁻⁻⁻

Insects at start = ... ÷ (.................)⁻⁻⁻⁻

= .... ÷ .... = ...

.... insects

[3]

    b)   How many insects will be in the tank after 13 weeks?

.... insects

[3]

[Total 6 marks]

3 Helen buys a new phone for £650.
The phone depreciates in value by 18% every year.

a) How much will the phone be worth after 3 years? Give your answer to the nearest penny.

£ ....

[3]

b) How many years will it take before the phone is worth less than a quarter of its original price?

.... years

[3]

[Total 6 marks]

4 Stephen is about to buy a TV that costs £899. He wants to borrow the money and pay back the full amount, with interest, after 2 years.

He finds the following two companies that will loan him the money:

Bushberg Ltd	**Weynell Bank**
Compound interest	Compound interest
First year 2%	First year 1%
Second year 3%	Second year 5%

How much less would Stephen pay by choosing the best value loan?
Give your answer to the nearest penny. You must show your working.

£ ....

[Total 4 marks]

Score:

21

Speed, Density and Pressure

1   The wooden block shown on the right has a mass of 2.5 kg.

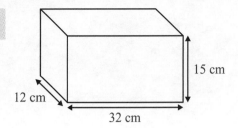

12 cm · 32 cm · 15 cm

a)   Calculate the volume of the block in cm³.

.... cm³

[2]

b)   Calculate the density of the block in g/cm³.
      Give your answer to one decimal place.

.... g/cm³

[3]

[Total 5 marks]

2   A triangular prism is standing on one of its triangular faces, which has
      a base of 4 m and a height of 5 m. The prism has a weight of 500 N.

a)   Calculate the pressure, in N/m², that the prism is exerting on the ground.

.... N/m²

[3]

b)   A force is applied to the top of the prism, increasing the pressure exerted
      on the ground by 6.5 N/m². Calculate the size of this force in N.

.... N

[2]

[Total 5 marks]

3   A long-distance runner completes a 45 km race in two and a half hours.

Calculate their average speed in m/s.

.... m/s
[Total 3 marks]

4   A car journey was made up of three parts.

•   The first part was 75 km and had an average speed of 50 km/h.
•   The second part was twice the distance of the first part and had an average speed of 60 km/h.
•   The third part was 10 km and had an average speed of 40 km/h.

How long did the entire journey take? Give your answer in minutes.

.... minutes
[Total 4 marks]

5   The density of a stone block is 2150 kg/m^3.
The volume of the block is 3 680 000 cm^3.

Calculate the mass of the block in g.

.... g
[Total 4 marks]

6 Becca is investigating the densities of different metals.

A mix of metals contains:
- 50 cm³ of zinc, which has a density of 7.14 g/cm³.
- 25 cm³ of tin, which has a density of 7.26 g/cm³.
- 20 cm³ of copper.

a) The entire mix has a mass of 717.7 g. Find the density of copper.
   Give your answer in g/cm³.

.... g/cm³

[4]

b) Becca wants to make the mixture as heavy as possible by adding an extra 10 cm³ of one of the three metals. Which metal should she choose? Explain your answer.

....

....

[2]

[Total 6 marks]

7 The pressure that a bag of sand exerts on the ground is 600 N/m².

More sand is added to the bag, which causes:
- the weight of the sand to double,
- the surface area of the bag that touches the ground to become four times bigger.

Find the pressure that the bag of sand now exerts on the ground.
Give your answer in N/m².

.... N/m²

[Total 2 marks]

Exam Practice Tip

The formulas for speed, density and pressure can each be condensed into one of those nifty formula triangles. In an exam, you might find it helpful to write down the relevant triangle at the start of a question, then use it to check you're using the right formula — but don't go saying any mnemonics you may know out loud...

Score

29

Congruent Triangles

1   Four triangles are drawn below.   Diagram not accurately drawn

A   **B**   **C**   **D**

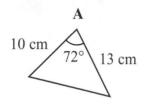 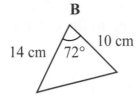 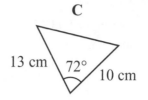 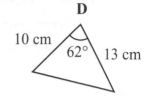

a)   Which **two** of the triangles are congruent?

.... and ....

[1]

b)   Circle the reason for your answer to part a).

SSS   AAS   SAS   RHS

[1]

[Total 2 marks]

2   The diagram below shows a regular hexagon made up of four triangles.

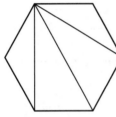

Diagram not
accurately drawn

Which of the following statements is true?
Tick the correct answer.

All four triangles are congruent

Exactly one pair of triangles are congruent

Exactly two pairs of triangles are congruent

None of the triangles are congruent

[Total 1 mark]

3   Triangles *ABC* and *DEF* are congruent.

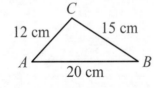   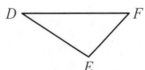   Diagram not
accurately drawn

a)   Circle the answer that describes triangle *DEF*.

equilateral   isosceles   scalene   obtuse

[1]

b)   ∠*CAB* = ∠*EFD*. What is the length of *DE*?

DE = ... cm

[1]

[Total 2 marks]

4 The diagram on the right is made up of two congruent triangles.

Find the size of the angle x.

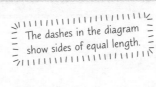

The dashes in the diagram show sides of equal length.

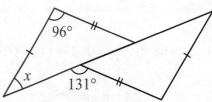

$x = \text{...................}^{\circ}$

[Total 2 marks]

5 Are the triangles *ABC* and *DEF* congruent?

Explain your answer.

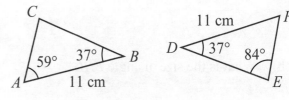

Diagram not accurately drawn

....

....

[Total 3 marks]

6 The shaded regions of the rectangle below are two congruent triangles.

Find the area of the rectangle that is **not** shaded.

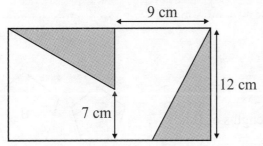

Diagram not accurately drawn

.... cm²

[Total 4 marks]

Exam Practice Tip

You need to know all four conditions for congruent triangles — SSS, AAS, SAS and RHS. They all require three bits of information and they're named after what's needed. For example, if you're given the size of two angles and the length of one side, that's A, A and S, so it's the AAS condition that you're after.

Score

14

Section Five — Shapes and Area

Similar Shapes

1   The shapes *ABCD* and *EFGH* are similar.

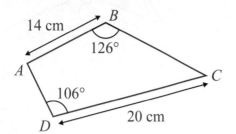

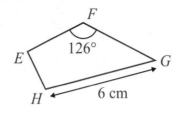

Diagrams not
accurately drawn

a)   Work out the length of *EF*.

EF = ... cm

[2]

b)   What is the size of angle *EHG*?

.....................°

[1]

[Total 3 marks]

2   Are these two triangles similar?

Explain your answer.

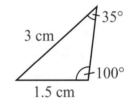

Diagram not
accurately drawn

....

....

[Total 2 marks]

3   Shapes A and B are similar regular pentagons.

The ratio of the side lengths of A to the side lengths of B is 3 : 7.
The perimeter of A is 12 cm.

Work out the perimeter of B.

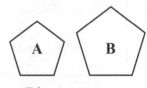

Diagram not
accurately drawn

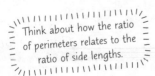
Think about how the ratio
of perimeters relates to the
ratio of side lengths.

.... cm

[Total 2 marks]

Section Five — Shapes and Area

4   Shoaib has drawn the diagram on the right.

The triangles *ACE* and *BCD* are similar.

a)   Work out the length of *EC*.

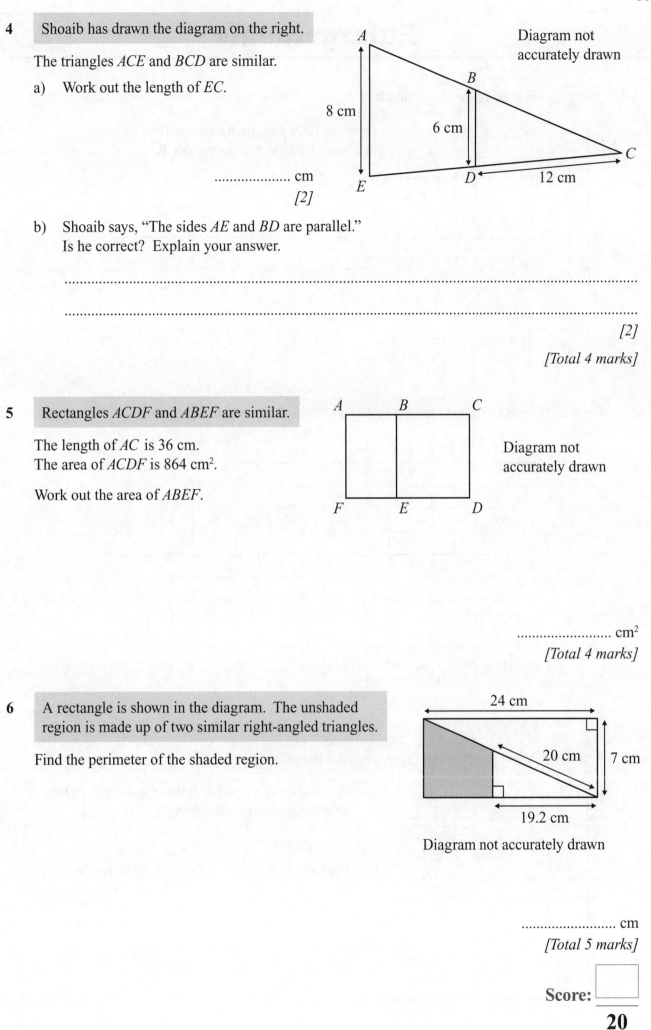

Diagram not accurately drawn

.... cm
[2]

b)   Shoaib says, "The sides *AE* and *BD* are parallel."
Is he correct? Explain your answer.

....

....

[2]

[Total 4 marks]

5   Rectangles *ACDF* and *ABEF* are similar.

The length of *AC* is 36 cm.
The area of *ACDF* is 864 cm².

Work out the area of *ABEF*.

Diagram not accurately drawn

.... cm²
[Total 4 marks]

6   A rectangle is shown in the diagram. The unshaded region is made up of two similar right-angled triangles.

Find the perimeter of the shaded region.

Diagram not accurately drawn

.... cm
[Total 5 marks]

Score:

20

Section Five — Shapes and Area

Enlargements

1 The diagram shows triangles **A** and **B**.

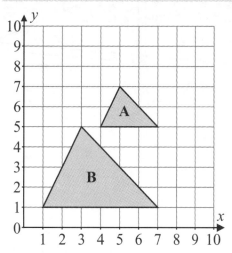

Describe fully a single transformation that maps triangle **A** onto triangle **B**.

....

....

....

[Total 3 marks]

2 On the grid, enlarge the shape by a scale factor of 3 with a centre of enlargement at point *P*.

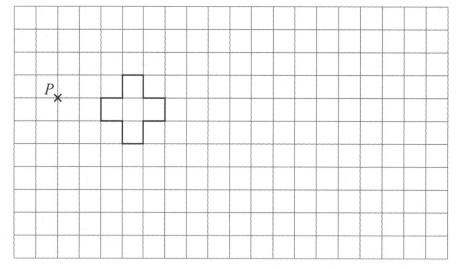

[Total 3 marks]

3 A triangle **A** and points *P* and *Q* are drawn on the grid below.

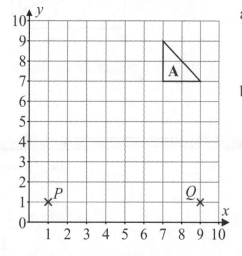

a) Plot and label a point *R* so that the triangle *PQR* is an enlargement of triangle **A**.

[1]

b) Find the scale factor and centre of this enlargement.

Scale factor: ....

Centre: (.........., ...)

[2]

[Total 3 marks]

4 On the grid, enlarge the shape by a scale factor of $\frac{1}{3}$ with a centre of enlargement at (–8, 5).

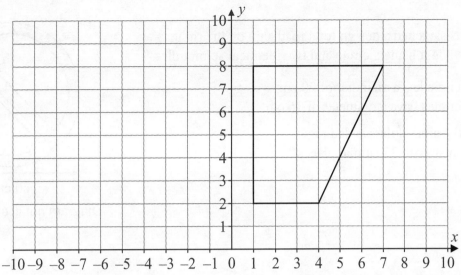

[Total 3 marks]

5 Shape **A** is obtained from shape **B** by an enlargement with a scale factor of $\frac{1}{4}$ and a centre of enlargement at (2, 9). Shape **A** is drawn on the grid below.

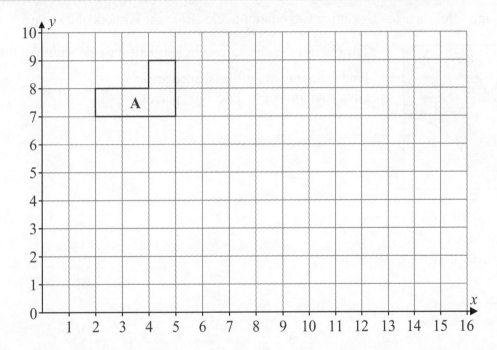

a) Draw the shape **B** on the grid.

[3]

b) Circle the word that describes shapes **A** and **B**.

congruent   reflected   similar   parallel

[1]

[Total 4 marks]

Score

16

Section Five — Shapes and Area

Perimeter and Area — Circles

1   Basma has sketched a design for a road sign on the right.
     She has made it using a circle and two identical semicircles.

The outer circle has a diameter of 20 cm.
Both semicircles have a diameter of 16 cm.

Calculate the area of the shaded region.
Give your answer to 2 decimal places.

16 cm

20 cm

Diagram not accurately drawn

.... cm²

[Total 3 marks]

2   The shape below is made by cutting two quarter circles from the corners of a square.

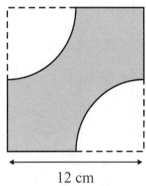

The radius of each quarter circle is half the side length of the square.

Find the perimeter of the shaded area.
Give your answer to 2 decimal places.

12 cm

Diagram not
accurately drawn

.... cm

[Total 3 marks]

3   A sector of a circle is shown on the right.

Show that the exact area of the sector is 3π cm².

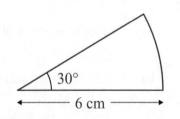

30°

6 cm

Diagram not accurately drawn

[Total 2 marks]

Section Five — Shapes and Area

4 A sector of a circle is shown on the right.

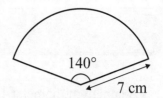

Diagram not accurately drawn

a) Find the arc length of the sector.
Give your answer to 2 decimal places.

.... cm
[2]

b) Hence find the perimeter of the sector.
Give your answer to 2 decimal places.

.... cm
[1]

[Total 3 marks]

5 The diagram on the right shows a sector of a circle of radius 5 cm inside a sector of a circle of radius 8 cm.

Diagram not accurately drawn

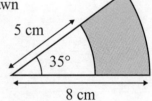

Work out the area of the shaded region.
Give your answer to 2 decimal places.

Area of large sector = $\dfrac{\text{................}}{360}$ × π × (.............)^2 = ... cm^2

Area of small sector = $\dfrac{\text{................}}{360}$ × π × (.............)^2 = ... cm^2

Area of shaded region = area of large sector — area of small sector

= .... — .... = ... cm^2

.... cm^2
[Total 4 marks]

6 The diagram below shows a sector with an arc length of 2π cm.

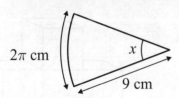

Find the exact size of the angle x.

Diagram not accurately drawn

$x =$ .... °
[Total 3 marks]

Score:

18

Section Five — Shapes and Area

Surface Area

1 A sphere of diameter 12 cm is shown below.

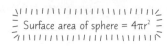
Surface area of sphere = $4\pi r^2$

Find the surface area of the sphere.
Give your answer to 2 significant figures.

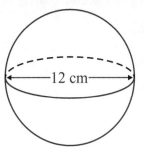

.... cm²
[Total 2 marks]

2 A cylinder has a height of 5.2 cm and a radius of 2.1 cm.

a) Estimate the surface area of the cylinder.

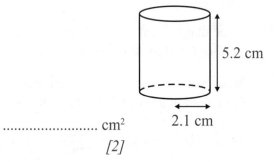
Surface area of cylinder:
$A = 2\pi rh + 2\pi r^2$

5.2 cm

2.1 cm

.... cm²
[2]

b) Is the actual surface area of the cylinder bigger or smaller than your estimate?
Give a reason for your answer.

....

....

[1]

[Total 3 marks]

3 The shape on the right is made up of four identical cubes.
Each cube has a volume of 8 cm³.

Find the total surface area of the shape.

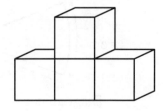

.... cm²
[Total 3 marks]

4 Isla has two identical models of the square-based pyramid shown in the diagram below.

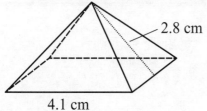

2.8 cm

4.1 cm

Diagram not accurately drawn

a) Find the surface area of the pyramid.
Give your answer to 2 decimal places.

.... cm²
[4]

b) Isla creates a new shape by gluing together the square sides of two models. How much smaller is the surface area of the new shape than the total surface area of the two models?

.... cm²
[1]

[Total 5 marks]

5 Bilal has a piece of wood in the shape of a cone, as shown below.

Surface area of cone = πr*l* + πr²
where *l* is the slant height.

a) Find the exact surface area of the cone.
Give your answer in terms of π.

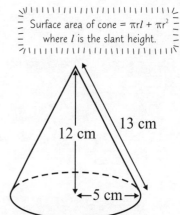

12 cm   13 cm

5 cm

.... cm²
[2]   Diagram not accurately drawn

b) Bilal cuts the cone into two equal pieces by cutting along the circle's diameter.

How much greater is the total surface area of the two pieces than the surface area of the original piece?

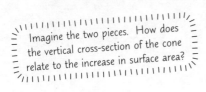

Imagine the two pieces. How does the vertical cross-section of the cone relate to the increase in surface area?

.... cm²
[2]

[Total 4 marks]

Score:

17

Section Five — Shapes and Area

Volumes

1   A square-based pyramid is shown in the diagram below.

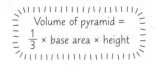

Volume of pyramid =
$\frac{1}{3}$ × base area × height

Find the volume of the pyramid.

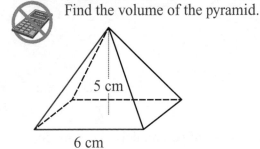

5 cm

6 cm

Diagram not accurately drawn

.... cm³

[Total 2 marks]

2   The triangular prism on the right has a volume of 624 cm³.

Find the length, *L* cm, of the prism.

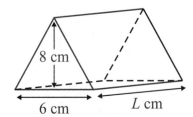

8 cm

6 cm   *L* cm

Diagram not accurately drawn

L = ...

[Total 3 marks]

3   A cone and a triangular prism are shown below.

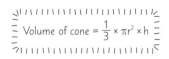

Volume of cone = $\frac{1}{3}$ × πr² × h

Find the ratio of their volumes in its simplest form.

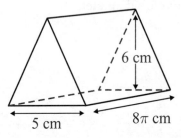

6 cm

5 cm   8π cm

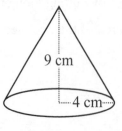

9 cm

4 cm

Diagram not accurately drawn

.... : ....

[Total 5 marks]

4   Jeanine buys a pack of three tennis balls. Each ball is a sphere with a radius of 3.2 cm.

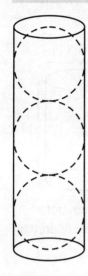

a)   Work out the volume of one tennis ball.
     Give your answer to 1 decimal place.

Volume of sphere = $\frac{4}{3}\pi r^3$

.... cm³

[2]

The balls come in a cylinder-shaped container that is just large enough to fit the balls stacked on top of each other, as shown in the diagram on the left.

b)   Jeanine says, "The volume of the container is 620 cm³ to 2 significant figures." Is she correct? Explain your answer.

....

....

[3]

[Total 5 marks]

5   A frustum is shaded in the diagram below.

Volume of cone = $\frac{1}{3} \times \pi r^2 \times h$

Find the exact volume of the frustum.
Give your answer in terms of π.

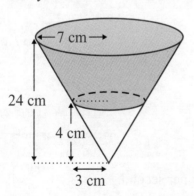

Diagram not accurately drawn

.... cm³

[Total 5 marks]

Exam Practice Tip

Don't worry — you'll be given the formula for the volume of a cone in your exam. The trickiest bit is knowing to use the vertical height rather than the slant height. You won't be told the formula for the volume of a frustum, but it's easy to put together (or take apart) if you think about how they're made.

Score

20

Rates of Flow

1   A can of carrot juice has the shape of a cylinder, as shown on the right.

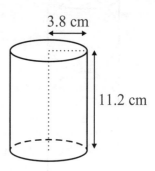

3.8 cm

11.2 cm

Diagram not
accurately drawn

A full can is emptied at a rate of 0.05 litres per second.

How long does it take to empty the can?
Give your answer to the nearest second.

1 litre = 1000 cm³

Volume of can = π × (.................)² × .... = ... cm³

0.05 litres per second = 0.05 × .... = ... cm³/s

So it will take .... ÷ .... = ... seconds.

.... seconds
[Total 3 marks]

2   Mariam has a swimming pool in the shape of a cuboid, as shown below.

1 litre = 1000 cm³

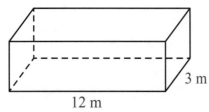

3 m

12 m

Diagram not accurately drawn

She fills the empty pool with water using a hose pipe
that has a rate of flow of 27 litres per minute.

How long does it take to fill the pool to a depth of 1.5 m?
Give your answer to the nearest hour.

.... hours
[Total 3 marks]

3   Keith buys a beach ball. It's shown fully inflated below.

Volume of sphere = $\frac{4}{3}\pi r^3$

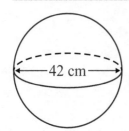

42 cm

The ball is bought flat and empty of air.
He inflates the ball at a rate of 8 litres of air per second.

How long does it take him to fully inflate the ball?
Give your answer to 1 significant figure.

.... seconds
[Total 3 marks]

4 Becky has a sand timer. She models its shape using two identical cones, as shown below.

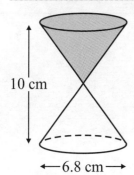

10 cm

←—6.8 cm—→

Diagram not
accurately drawn

The timer contains enough sand to fill one cone.
The sand drains from the top cone to the bottom
cone at a rate of 2 cm³ per second.

Volume of cone = $\frac{1}{3} \times \pi r^2 \times h$

Explain how Becky could use the timer to measure approximately one minute.
You must show your working.

Start by finding how long
it takes the sand to drain
from top to bottom.

....

....

[Total 4 marks]

5 A factory fills bags of flour using a funnel in the shape of a
square-based pyramid, as shown in the diagram on the right.

Volume of pyramid =
$\frac{1}{3}$ × base area × height

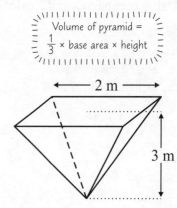

←— 2 m —→

3 m

Flour pours from the funnel at a rate of 120 cm³ per second.

a) How many hours does it take to empty a full funnel?
Give your answer in hours, correct to 2 decimal places.

.... hours
[3]

b) A full bag of flour has a volume of 946 cm³.
How many bags could the factory fill in two hours?
Give your answer to the nearest hundred.

.... bags
[2]

[Total 5 marks]

Score:

18

Section Five — Shapes and Area

Loci and Construction

1   The triangular field below has a security system which will detect any movement outside of the field within 3 m of its perimeter.

Shade the region that the system covers.

Scale: 1 cm
represents 3 m

[Total 2 marks]

2   Martha has drawn the equilateral triangle shown below.

She wants to draw an isosceles triangle that has:
*   the same length base as the equilateral triangle
*   two 30° angles

Using compasses and a ruler only, construct the isosceles triangle.

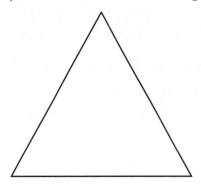

You can draw the isosceles triangle inside the equilateral triangle.

[Total 3 marks]

3   Rectangle *R* is shown below.

Shade the region within *R* that is:
*   more than 2 m from point *S*
*   closer to point *S* than point *T*

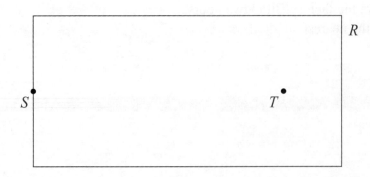

Scale: 1 cm
represents 1 m

[Total 4 marks]

4 A mayor is deciding where to place a new statue in a park.
The park contains two perpendicular footpaths, *L* and *M*.

The statue must be:
- exactly 5 m away from the footpaths *L* and *M*
- within 15 m of the bench *B*

Mark the possible locations for the statue with a cross.

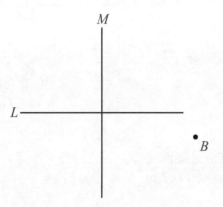

Scale: 1 cm
represents 5 m

[Total 3 marks]

5 Sven's back garden is shown below.
He is deciding where to plant a tree.

The tree must be:
- closer to *AD* than *AB*
- at least 3 m away from corners *C* and *D*

Shade the region where the tree could go.

Scale: 1 cm
represents 2 m

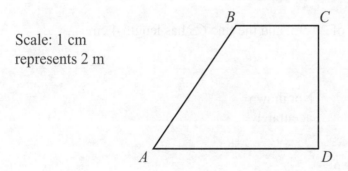

[Total 5 marks]

Score

17

Section Six — Angles and Geometry

Pythagoras' Theorem

1 The rectangle *ABCD* is shown on the right.

What is the length of *AC*?

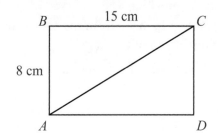

$AC =$ .... cm

[Total 3 marks]

2 Greg leans a 7 m ladder against a vertical wall. The distance between the base of the ladder and the base of the wall is 2 m.

How high up the wall does the ladder reach?
Give your answer to 1 d.p.

.... m

[Total 3 marks]

3 The shape *QRST* is made up of four identical right-angled triangles meeting at the point *C*, as shown below.

The diamond has a total perimeter of 20 cm, and the line *CS* has length 4 cm.
Work out the length of *RT*.

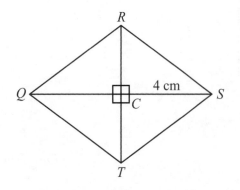

Not drawn
accurately

$RT =$ .... cm

[Total 4 marks]

4   Claire claims she has drawn a right-angled triangle whose sides are 5 cm, 12 cm and 14 cm long.
Do you think Claire is correct? Explain your answer.

....

....

[Total 2 marks]

5   Pentagon *ABCDE* shown below is made up of two identical right-angled triangles and a square.

Given that *AB* = 10 m and *BC* = 12 m, find the length of the line *AF*.

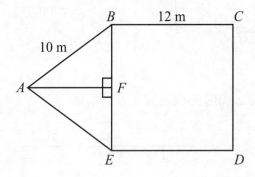

Not drawn
accurately

AF = ... m

[Total 4 marks]

6   The parallelogram *ABCD* is shown below.
AE : *ED* = 1 : 3, *AB* = 15 cm and *ED* = 27 cm.

Find the area of the parallelogram.

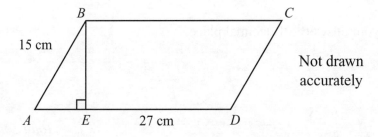

Not drawn
accurately

.... cm²

[Total 4 marks]

Score:

20

Section Six — Angles and Geometry

Trigonometry

1 The diagram on the right shows a right-angled triangle.

Find *m*, giving your answer to 1 decimal place.

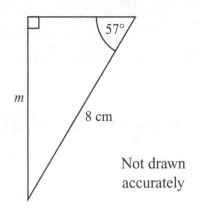

57°

m

8 cm

Not drawn accurately

m = ... cm

[Total 2 marks]

2 Rajesh is using the right-angled triangle below to find the value of cos *x*.

a) Look at his working below. Explain the mistake he has made and give the correct value of cos *x*.

$$\cos x = \frac{o}{h} = \frac{3}{5} = 0.6$$

4 cm

x

5 cm

3 cm

Not drawn accurately

....

....

[2]

b) Hence find angle *x*, giving your answer to 1 decimal place.

x = ... °

[1]

[Total 3 marks]

3 The diagram shows a right-angled triangle.

Find angle *x*, giving your answer to 1 decimal place.

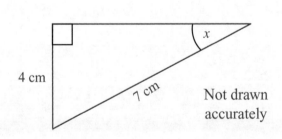

x

4 cm

7 cm

Not drawn accurately

x = ... °

[Total 2 marks]

4 Work out the exact value for each of the following calculations.

a) $\sin 60° + \cos 30°$

....

[2]

b) $4\cos 60° + \sin 90°$

....

[2]

c) $3\tan 45° - 4\sin 30°$

....

[2]

[Total 6 marks]

5 The diagram shows a right-angled triangle.

Find the exact value of angle x.

.... $x = \dfrac{O}{A}$

.... $x = \dfrac{\text{..............}}{\text{..............}}$ = ...

$x =$ .... $^{-1}($..............$)$ = ...$°$

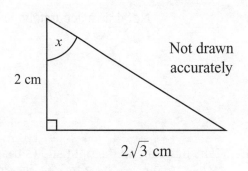

Not drawn accurately

2 cm

$2\sqrt{3}$ cm

$x =$ ....$°$

[Total 2 marks]

6 The diagram below shows rectangle *ABCD*.

$CD = 2.5$ cm and $CD : BC = 1 : 2$.
Find angle x, giving your answer to 1 decimal place.

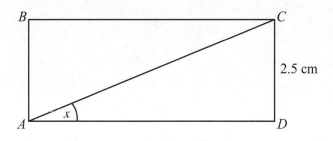

2.5 cm

Not drawn accurately

$x =$ ....$°$

[Total 3 marks]

Section Six — Angles and Geometry

76

7 The diagram shows a right-angled triangle *ABC* contained within a circle of radius $\sqrt{2}$ cm and centre *O*. Angle *BAC* = 33°.

Find the length of *AB*, giving your answer to 1 decimal place.

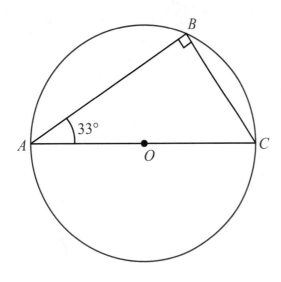

Not drawn accurately

AB = ... cm

[Total 3 marks]

8 The diagram on the right shows triangle *ABC*. *AB* = 17 cm. Angle *BAC* : Angle *BCA* = 3 : 7.

Find the length of *BC*, giving your answer to 1 decimal place.

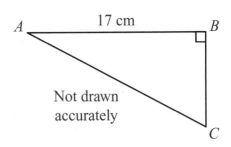

Not drawn accurately

BC = ... cm

[Total 4 marks]

Vectors

1 The diagram below shows two vectors, **u** and **v**, on a grid of unit squares.

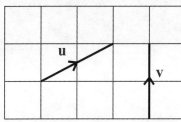

a) Write **u** and **v** as column vectors.

u = ..., **v** = ...
[2]

b) Calculate the following, giving your answers as column vectors.
   i) **u** – 4**v**

....
[1]

   ii) $3\mathbf{u} + \frac{1}{2}\mathbf{v}$

....
[1]

[Total 4 marks]

2 *ABCD* is a parallelogram. $\overrightarrow{AB}$ = 2**a** and $\overrightarrow{CB}$ = –**b**. *M* is the midpoint of *CD*.

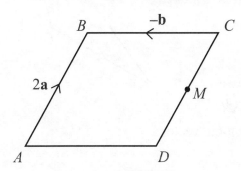

Write in terms of **a** and **b**:

a) $\overrightarrow{AC}$

....
[2]

b) $\overrightarrow{DM}$

....
[2]

c) $\overrightarrow{MA}$

....
[2]

[Total 6 marks]

3   The diagram below shows a grid of unit squares.

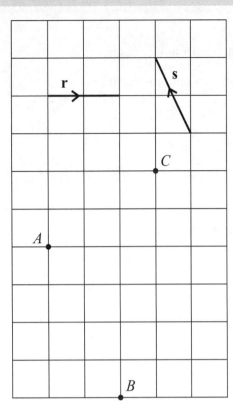

Write in terms of **r** and **s**:

a) $\overrightarrow{AB}$

....
[1]

b) $\overrightarrow{AC}$

....
[1]

c) $\overrightarrow{BC}$

....
[1]

[Total 3 marks]

4   *ABC* is a triangle. $\overrightarrow{CA} = -\mathbf{c} - 3\mathbf{d}$ and $\overrightarrow{CB} = 2\mathbf{c} + 2\mathbf{d}$. *S* is the midpoint of *BC*.

a)   Write $\overrightarrow{AS}$ in terms of **c** and **d**:

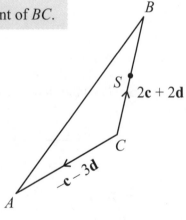

....
[3]

b)   Given that $\mathbf{c} = \begin{pmatrix} -1 \\ 3 \end{pmatrix}$ and $\mathbf{d} = \begin{pmatrix} 4 \\ 2 \end{pmatrix}$, express $\overrightarrow{AS}$ as a column vector.

....
[1]

[Total 4 marks]

Score:

17

Probability Experiments

1   Imran tosses a coin 150 times. It lands on heads 63 times.

a)   Work out the relative frequency of the coin landing on tails.

....

[1]

b)   Imran says, "The more I flip the coin, the closer the relative frequency will get to 0.5."
Give one reason why he may be wrong.

....

....

[1]

[Total 2 marks]

2   Henry and Jan are playing noughts and crosses.
The table below shows the results after a number of games.

Outcome	Henry won	Jan won	Draw
Relative frequency	0.17	?	0.53

Estimate the number of times Jan would win if they played 60 games.

....

[Total 2 marks]

3   Katy has a 5-sided spinner that is labelled A-E.
She spins it 80 times and records the results in the table below.

Letter	A	B	C	D	E
Frequency	10	18	16	12	
Relative frequency	0.125	0.225			

a)   Complete the table.

[2]

b)   Katy spins the spinner another 120 times.
Estimate the number of times it will land on a letter other than E.

....

[2]

[Total 4 marks]

4 Fred plays chess against two of his friends. The table shows how many games he won and lost against each.

	Elyse	Nige
Won	16	27
Lost	34	13

a) Estimate the probabilities of Fred winning a game of chess against each of his friends.

Elyse: ....   Nige: ....

[3]

b) Which of your two answers is the more reliable estimate? Explain your answer.

....

....

[1]

[Total 4 marks]

5 Lin has a pack of cards. She picks one card at random and guesses whether it's red or black, then checks if she's right before putting it back and shuffling the pack. She does this 200 times.

She guessed red $\frac{5}{8}$ of the times and got 64 correct.
Of the times she guessed black, she got 33 correct.

a) Complete the frequency tree below to show her results.

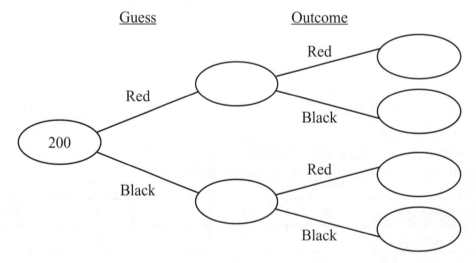

[2]

b) Estimate the probability of Lin guessing the colour correctly.

....

[2]

[Total 4 marks]

Score:

16

The AND/OR Rules

1   Nancy and Trevor both enter a prize draw.
Their names are put into a hat with the names of 23 other contestants.

A winning name is picked at random from the hat.
What is the probability that either Nancy or Trevor wins?

....

[Total 2 marks]

2   Ryan has 1 red marble, 3 green marbles and 5 blue marbles in a bag.
He asks people to pick a marble at random from the bag and then replace it.

 What is the probability that two people in a row pick a red marble?

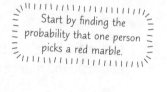
Start by finding the
probability that one person
picks a red marble.

....

[Total 2 marks]

3   Haley and Kim each roll a dice numbered 1-6. Haley's dice is unbiased.

The probability of Kim's dice landing on each number is given in this table.

Number	1	2	3	4	5	6
Probability	0.2	0.3	0.2	0.1	0.1	0.1

a)   What is the probability that Kim's dice lands on a 1 or a 6?

....

[2]

b)   What is the probability that both Haley and Kim's dice lands on a 1 or a 6?

P(Haley rolling a 1 or 6) = $\frac{............}{6}$

P(Haley and Kim rolling a 1 or 6) = P(Haley rolling a 1 or 6) × P(Kim rolling a 1 or 6)

= .... × ....

= ....

....

[3]

[Total 5 marks]

Section Seven — Probability and Statistics

4   On weekdays, Quinn buys her lunch at a school canteen. The probability that she buys a brownie doubles every day, beginning on Monday at 0.05.

What is the probability that she buys a brownie on Thursday but not Friday?

> *Start by finding the probability that she buys a brownie on each day of the week.*

....

[Total 3 marks]

5   Pablo has two fair spinners which are shown below. Each spinner is split into equal sectors.

Spinner A   Spinner B

He spins them together and records the results. He repeats this 160 times.
Estimate the number of times that both spinners land on 4.

....

[Total 4 marks]

6   Alex and Kari are playing darts. The probability that Alex hits the bullseye with one dart is 0.6, and the probability that Kari hits the bullseye with one dart is 0.3.

They each throw one dart.
What is the probability that at least one of them hits the bullseye?

> *Use the probability that they both miss the bullseye.*

....

[Total 4 marks]

Exam Practice Tip

If you're mixing up your AND/OR rules, remember this — the probability of both events happening has to be less than the probability of just one of them happening, and the probability of either happening is greater. So if your answer doesn't agree with this, then it's a sure bet that you've used the wrong rule.

Score

20

Tree Diagrams

1 Kyle goes to a cinema. The probability that he buys a drink is 0.9, and the probability that he buys popcorn is 0.8.

a) Complete the tree diagram below.

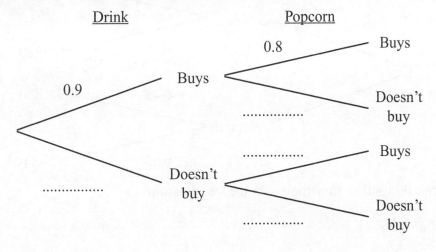

[2]

b) What is the probability that Kyle buys popcorn but not a drink?

....

[2]

[Total 4 marks]

2 Riya is playing a game with an ordinary and fair 6-sided dice. She must roll a 5 or a 6 to win. If she doesn't win on her first attempt, she can roll the dice again but then must roll a 6 to win.

a) Complete the tree diagram below.

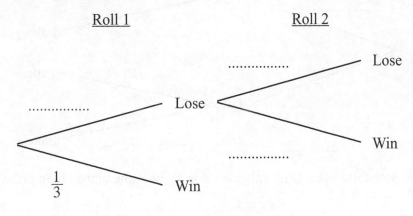

[2]

b) What is the probability that Riya wins the game?

....

[3]

[Total 5 marks]

Section Seven — Probability and Statistics

3   Mark has a bag of coloured counters. He picks one at random. The probability that it's coloured red is 0.45. He replaces the counter and then picks another one at random.

Mark draws this tree diagram to show the possible outcomes.

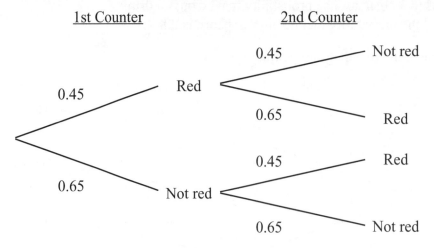

Write down **two** things that are wrong with the tree diagram.

....

....

....

[Total 2 marks]

4   Gail walks her dog either at a park or a lake. The probability that she goes to the park is 0.7, unless she was at the park the day before, in which case the probability is 0.6.

a)   Given that Gail walked her dog at the lake on Friday, complete the tree diagram below.

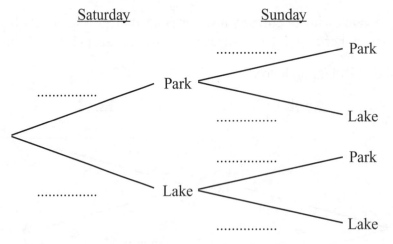

[2]

b)   What is the probability that Gail walks her dog at the same place on Saturday and Sunday?

....

[3]

[Total 5 marks]

Score:

16

Sets and Venn Diagrams

1   A cafe served 100 customers. 59 customers bought coffee, 67 customers bought cake, and 44 customers bought both coffee and cake.

a)   Complete the Venn diagram below.

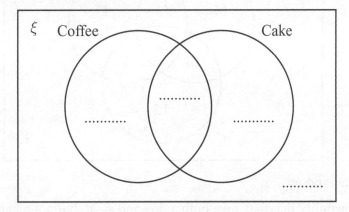

[3]

b)   A customer was chosen at random.
What is the probability that they bought coffee or cake, but not both?

....
[2]

[Total 5 marks]

2   ξ = { even integers < 20 }
A = { 2, 6, 8, 12, 14, 18 }
B = { 2, 4, 14, 16 }

   a)   Complete the Venn diagram below to show all the elements in each set.

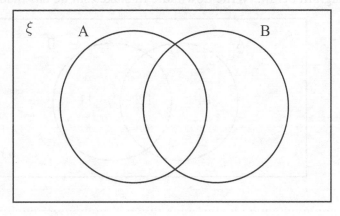

[3]

b)   An element of ξ is chosen at random.
What is the probability that it is a member of A ∪ B?

....
[2]

[Total 5 marks]

Section Seven — Probability and Statistics

3   Vinnie asks 100 people if they own a dog (A), a cat (B) or a hamster (C).
His results are shown in the Venn diagram below.

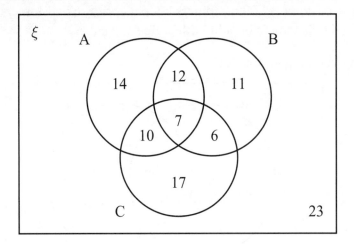

A person is chosen at random.

a)   What is the probability that they own both a dog and a cat, but not a hamster?

....

[2]

b)   Vinnie says, "They are more likely to own a hamster than to own none of the three pets."
Is he correct? Explain your answer.

....

....

[2]

c)   Vinnie wants to look at the results for cat or dog owners only.
He draws the diagram below. Write down **one** mistake that he has made.

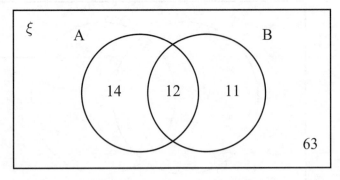

....

....

[1]

[Total 5 marks]

Score:

15

Mean, Median, Mode and Range

1 The data below shows the number of fouls made by players in a football team over a full season.

```
0 | 5
1 | 2 6
2 | 4 4 7 8
3 | 2 6 8
4 | 4
```

Key
0	7 means
7 fouls

Find the mean number of fouls made by a player.

....

[Total 2 marks]

2 The data shows the masses of some balls at a bowling alley.

```
5 | 6 9
6 | 2 5 8
7 | 1 3
```

Key
1	5 means
1.5 kg

a) Work out the range of this data.
Comment on this value as a measure of the spread.

....

....

[2]

b) Find the mean mass of a ball. Give your answer to 1 decimal place.

.... kg
[2]

[Total 4 marks]

3 Seren writes down some positive integers. She covers the median, m, and another number, x.

(25) (13) (14) (28) (15) (   ) (   )

a) The range of the set is 29. Find the value of x.

$x =$ ....
[1]

b) The mean of the set is 22. Find the value of m.

$m =$ ....
[2]

[Total 3 marks]

Section Seven — Probability and Statistics

4 Two groups of 5 children measure their height.
The results are shown in the table on the right.

	Height (cm)	
	Median	**Mean**
Group A	124	127
Group B	132	131

A child who is 125 cm tall moves from Group A to Group B.

a) Can you tell if the median for Group A will have changed?
Explain your answer.

....

....

[1]

b) Find the new mean height for both groups.

Group A: .... cm   Group B: .... cm

[4]

[Total 5 marks]

5 The ages of members of a book club are shown below. Their total age is 245.

```
1 | 6
2 | 2 3 8
3 | 9
5 | 4
6 | 3
```

Key
1	7 means
17 years old

Two people leave the club and the mean age increases by 5.
How old were they?

.... and ....
[Total 4 marks]

Exam Practice Tip

You need to be able to calculate the different averages and the range, but you also need to understand what they tell you about the data and how they're affected when the data changes. Don't be afraid to say when you think something can't be determined by the given information — sometimes that's the right answer!

Score

18

Grouped Frequency Tables

1 Parvati measured the lengths of some leaves that fell from a tree.

She has organised her results in the table below.

Length, l (cm)	Frequency
$6 < l \le 8$	11
$8 < l \le 10$	24
$10 < l \le 12$	15
$12 < l \le 14$	10

a) Write down the modal class.

....

[1]

b) Find the class that contains the median.

....

[2]

[Total 3 marks]

2 John measures the mass of the cereal he eats for breakfast.

This table shows the data he obtained in two different months.

Mass, m (grams)	Frequency	
	January	February
$20 < m \le 25$	4	5
$25 < m \le 30$	9	10
$30 < m \le 35$	10	13
$35 < m \le 45$	8	0

a) Work out an estimate for the range of the masses over both months.

Estimate of range = highest possible mass − lowest possible mass

= .... − .... = ... g

.... g

[1]

b) John says, "The median mass was higher in February than in January."
Is he correct? Explain your answer.

....

....

....

[3]

[Total 4 marks]

Section Seven — Probability and Statistics

3 The table below shows the time that people spent waiting for a bus.

Time, t (minutes)	Frequency		
$0 < t \leq 2$	6		
$2 < t \leq 4$	9		
$4 < t \leq 6$	6		
$6 < t \leq 8$	3		
$8 < t \leq 10$	1		
Total:			

Work out an estimate for the mean wait time.

.... minutes

[Total 3 marks]

4 Audrey records the height of some trees she planted a year ago.

She has organised her results in the table below.

Height, h (cm)	Frequency	Mid-interval value	Freq × mid-interval value
$0 < h \leq 15$	5	$(0 + 15) \div 2 = 7.5$	$5 \times 7.5 = 37.5$
$15 < h \leq 30$	9		
$30 < h \leq 45$	10		
$45 < h \leq 60$	6		
Total:			

a) Work out an estimate of the mean height.

.... cm

[4]

b) Explain how Audrey could make a more accurate estimate of the mean by changing the size and number of classes.

....

....

[1]

[Total 5 marks]

Score:

15

Section Seven — Probability and Statistics

Answers

Section One — Number

Pages 3-4: LCM and HCF

1. a) LCM = $2^3 \times 5^3 \times 7$ *[1 mark]*
   b) HCF = 2×5^2 *[1 mark]*

2. a) LCM = $3^6 \times 5^7 \times 11^6$ *[1 mark]*
   b) HCF = $3^4 \times 5^3 \times 11^5$ *[1 mark]*

3. a) $12 = 2^2 \times 3$ *[1 mark]*, so LCM = $2^2 \times 3^4 \times 5^3$ *[1 mark]*
   [2 marks available in total — as above]
   b) $18 = 2 \times 3^2$ *[1 mark]*, so HCF = 2×3 *[1 mark]*
   [2 marks available in total — as above]

4. Multiples of 12 are: 12, 24, 36, 48, 60, 72, 84, <u>96</u>, 108, ...
   Multiples of 24 are: 24, 48, 72, <u>96</u>, 120, 144, ...
   Multiples of 32 are: 32, 64, <u>96</u>, 128, ...
   The LCM of 12, 24 and 32 is 96, which is the smallest number of skips they need to complete.
   The smallest number of sets Dan needs to complete is:
   $96 \div 12 = 8$ sets.
   The smallest number of sets Jess needs to complete is:
   $96 \div 24 = 4$ sets.
   The smallest number of sets Sufjan needs to complete is:
   $96 \div 32 = 3$ sets.
   [3 marks available — 1 mark for a correct method to find LCM, 1 mark for LCM correct, 1 mark for all numbers of sets correct]

5. Multiples of 18 are: 18, 36, 54, 72, 90, 108, 126, 144, 162, <u>180</u>
   Multiples of 20 are: 20, 40, 60, 80, 100, 120, 140, 160, <u>180</u>
   Multiples of 36 are: 36, 72, 108, 144, <u>180</u>
   The LCM of 18, 20 and 36 is 180, which is the smallest number of each item she could buy.
   The smallest number of packs of envelopes she needs to buy is
   $180 \div 18 = 10$ packs.
   The smallest number of packs of stamps she needs to buy is
   $180 \div 20 = 9$ packs.
   The smallest number of packs of cards she needs to buy is
   $180 \div 36 = 5$ packs.
   [3 marks available — 1 mark for a correct method to find LCM, 1 mark for LCM correct, 1 mark for all numbers of packs correct]

6. Factors of 42 are: 1, 2, 3, 6, 7, 14, <u>21</u>, 42
   Factors of 63 are: 1, 3, 7, 9, <u>21</u>, 63
   Factors of 84 are: 1, 2, 3, 4, 6, 7, 12, 14, <u>21</u>, 28, 42, 84
   The HCF of 42, 63 and 84 is 21, so Ami makes 21 sandwiches.
   The number of cheese slices on each sandwich is
   $42 \div 21 = 2$ slices.
   The number of apple slices on each sandwich is
   $63 \div 21 = 3$ slices.
   The number of tomato slices on each sandwich is
   $84 \div 21 = 4$ slices.
   [3 marks available — 1 mark for a correct method to find HCF, 1 mark for HCF correct, 1 mark for all correct number of slices]
   You could use prime factors to solve these wordy LCM/HCF problems, but listing the multiples or factors is much simpler, and your method will be easier to spot when your answer is marked.

Pages 5-6: Fractions

1. $\frac{7}{9}$ of $7\frac{7}{8} = 7\frac{7}{8} \times \frac{7}{9} = \frac{63}{8} \times \frac{7}{9} = \frac{63 \times 7}{8 \times 9} = \frac{7 \times \cancel{9} \times 7}{8 \times \cancel{9}} = \frac{49}{8} = 6\frac{1}{8}$
   [2 marks available in total — 1 mark for multiplying by the reciprocal fraction, 1 mark for the correct answer]

2. $\frac{5}{6} = \frac{5 \times 9}{6 \times 9} = \frac{45}{54}$, $\frac{11}{9} = \frac{11 \times 6}{9 \times 6} = \frac{66}{54}$ and $1 = \frac{54}{54}$
   $\frac{54}{54} - \frac{45}{54} = \frac{9}{54}$ and $\frac{66}{54} - \frac{54}{54} = \frac{12}{54}$. So $\frac{5}{6}$ is closer to 1.
   [3 marks available — 1 mark for writing both fractions over a common denominator, 1 mark for calculating the difference between each fraction and 1, 1 mark for the correct answer]

3. $1 - \frac{8}{15} = \frac{15}{15} - \frac{8}{15} = \frac{7}{15}$ *[1 mark]* of the eggs are not brown.
   So $\frac{5}{7} \times \frac{7}{15}$ *[1 mark]* $= \frac{5}{15} = \frac{1}{3}$ *[1 mark]* of the chickens.
   [3 marks available in total — as above]

4. $\frac{2}{3}$ of one team is $\frac{2}{3} \div 2 = \frac{2}{6} = \frac{1}{3}$ of all the players, and
   $\frac{4}{5}$ of the other team is $\frac{4}{5} \div 2 = \frac{4}{10} = \frac{2}{5}$ of all the players.
   So $\frac{1}{3} + \frac{2}{5} = \frac{5}{15} + \frac{6}{15} = \frac{11}{15}$ of the players are wearing black boots.
   [3 marks available — 1 mark for dividing each fraction by 2, 1 mark for a correct method of adding the resulting fractions, 1 mark for the correct answer]
   You could have added the fractions first and then divided. You'd still get the marks as long as you did it all correctly. This method would work for the next question too.

5. $\frac{2}{5}$ of the first shelf is $\frac{2}{5} \div 3 = \frac{2}{15}$ of the books, and
   $\frac{1}{4}$ of the second shelf is $\frac{1}{4} \div 3 = \frac{1}{12}$ of the books.
   So $\frac{2}{15} + \frac{1}{12} = \frac{8}{60} + \frac{5}{60} = \frac{13}{60}$ of the books are poetry.
   [3 marks available — 1 mark for dividing each fraction by 3, 1 mark for a correct method for adding the resulting fractions, 1 mark for the correct answer]

6. Balloon party income: $70 \times \frac{3}{14} = 15$ parties, $£90 \times 15 = £1350$
   Clown party income: $70 \times \frac{5}{14} = 25$ parties, $£96 \times 25 = £2400$
   Magic party income: $70 - 15 - 25 = 30$ parties, $£100 \times 30 = £3000$
   Total income $= £1350 + £2400 + £3000 = £6750$
   So $\frac{3000}{6750} = \frac{4}{9}$ of Sarah's income came from magic parties.
   [4 marks available — 2 marks for calculating the correct income for all three party types (otherwise, 1 mark for calculating the correct income for at least one party type), 1 mark for the correct total income £6750, 1 mark for the correct simplified answer]

7. $\frac{1}{3} \times \frac{3}{4} = \frac{1}{4}$ *[1 mark]* of the jeans are regular and blue.
   Total number of pairs of jeans $= 42 \div \frac{1}{4} = 168$ *[1 mark]*
   $1 - \frac{1}{3} - \frac{4}{7} = \frac{2}{21}$ of the jeans are baggy. *[1 mark]*
   $\frac{2}{21} \times \frac{3}{4} = \frac{1}{14}$ of the jeans are baggy and blue. *[1 mark]*
   So number of pairs of baggy blue jeans $= 168 \times \frac{1}{14} = 12$ *[1 mark]*
   [5 marks available in total — as above]

Pages 7-8: Rounding Errors

1 Sanya's height is rounded to the nearest 10 cm. It could be up to $10 \div 2 = 5$ cm smaller, so the minimum is $160 - 5 = 155$ cm. *[1 mark]*

2 The popcorn's mass could be up to $1 \div 2 = 0.5$ g bigger or smaller.
Minimum mass = $216 - 0.5 = 215.5$ g *[1 mark]*
Maximum mass = $216 + 0.5 = 216.5$ g *[1 mark]*
[2 marks available in total — as above]

3 E.g. Yes. To buy the bus ticket, Laura's shopping must cost less than £38 – £2.50 = £35.50.   The actual cost is £35 to the nearest pound, so it's definitely less than £35.50.
[2 marks available — 1 mark for the correct answer,
1 mark for a correct explanation]

4 a) Smallest possible value of $x = 6.4 - 0.05 = 6.35$
Largest possible value of $x = 6.4 + 0.05 = 6.45$
So the error interval is $6.35 \le x < 6.45$.
[2 marks available — 1 mark for $6.35 \le x$,
1 mark for $x < 6.45$]

   b) Smallest possible value of $y = 7.20 - 0.005 = 7.195$
Largest possible value of $y = 7.20 + 0.005 = 7.205$
So the error interval is $7.195 \le y < 7.205$.
[2 marks available — 1 mark for $7.195 \le y$,
1 mark for $y < 7.205$]

5 a) Smallest possible value of $T = 24.7 - 0.05 = 24.65$
Largest possible value of $T = 24.7 + 0.05 = 24.75$
So the error interval is $24.65 \le T < 24.75$.
[2 marks available — 1 mark for $24.65 \le T$,
1 mark for $T < 24.75$]

   b) The second timer gives a maximum possible value of $24.65 + 0.005 = 24.655$. From part a), you know that 24.65 is already the minimum possible value of T.
So the interval is $24.65 \le T < 24.655$.
[2 marks available — 1 mark for $24.65 \le T$,
1 mark for $T < 24.655$]

6 Each number could be up to $10 \div 2 = 5$ smaller. *[1 mark]*
So the total could be up to $5 \times 4 = 20$ smaller.
Minimum possible total = $110 - 20 = 90$ cars *[1 mark]*
[2 marks available — as above]

7 a) Smallest possible value of $L = 5 - 0.5 = 4.5$ cm
Largest possible value of $L = 5 + 0.5 = 5.5$ cm
So the error interval is 4.5 cm $\le L < 5.5$ cm.
[2 marks available — 1 mark for 4.5 cm $\le L$,
1 mark for $L < 5.5$ cm]

   b) Smallest possible value of $P = 4.5 \times 3 = 13.5$ cm
Largest possible value of $P = 5.5 \times 3 = 16.5$ cm
So the error interval is 13.5 cm $\le P < 16.5$ cm.
[2 marks available — 1 mark for 13.5 cm $\le P$,
1 mark for $P < 16.5$ cm]

Page 9: Powers

1 a) $\dfrac{5^2 \times 5^4}{5^3} = \dfrac{5^{(2+4)}}{5^3} = \dfrac{5^6}{5^3} = 5^6 \div 5^3 = 5^{(6-3)} = 5^3$ *[1 mark]*

   b) $(7^6)^3 \div 7^3 = 7^{(6 \times 3)} \div 7^3 = 7^{18} \div 7^3 = 7^{(18-3)} = 7^{15}$ *[1 mark]*

2 a) $3^{-2} = \dfrac{1}{3^2} = \dfrac{1}{9}$ *[1 mark]*

   b) $2^{-4} \times 2^7 = 2^{(-4+7)} = 2^3 = 8$ *[1 mark]*

   c) $7^{-3} \div 7^{-5} = 7^{(-3--5)} = 7^{(-3+5)} = 7^2 = 49$ *[1 mark]*

3 a) $(4^3 \times 4^2)^{-1} = (4^{(3+2)})^{-1} = (4^5)^{-1} = 4^{-5}$ *[1 mark]*
So $4^7 \times (4^3 \times 4^2)^{-1} = 4^7 \times 4^{-5} = 4^{(7-5)} = 4^2 = 16$ *[1 mark]*
[2 marks available in total — as above]

   b) $2^{-2} \times 2^{-3} = 2^{(-2+-3)} = 2^{-5}$ *[1 mark]*
So $(2^{-2} \times 2^{-3}) \div 2^{-9} = 2^{-5} \div 2^{-9} = 2^{(-5--9)} = 2^4 = 16$ *[1 mark]*
[2 marks available in total — as above]

Pages 10-11: Standard Form

1 a) 528 000 *[1 mark]*

   b) 9.762×10^{-4} *[1 mark]*

   c) $\dfrac{(7 \times 10^3) \times (3 \times 10^{-5})}{2.5 \times 10^2} = \dfrac{0.21}{250} = 0.00084$ or 8.4×10^{-4}
[2 marks available — 1 mark for a correct method,
1 mark for the correct answer]
Your calculator may be able to work this out all in one go,
but you'll lose out on marks if you don't write down the steps.

2 a) $(3 \times 10^2) \times (4 \times 10^3) = (3 \times 4) \times (10^2 \times 10^3)$ *[1 mark]*
$= 12 \times 10^{(2+3)} = 12 \times 10^5$
$= 1.2 \times 10^6$ *[1 mark]*
[2 marks available in total — as above]

   b) $(8 \times 10^7) \div (2 \times 10^4) = (8 \div 2) \times (10^7 \div 10^4)$ *[1 mark]*
$= 4 \times 10^{(7-4)} = 4 \times 10^3$ *[1 mark]*
[2 marks available in total — as above]

3 $(2.3 \times 10^4) \times (4 \times 10^{-3}) = (2.3 \times 4) \times (10^4 \times 10^{-3})$
$= 9.2 \times 10^{(4-3)} = 9.2 \times 10 = 92$ g
[2 marks available — 1 mark for a correct method of multiplying
the two numbers, 1 mark for the correct answer]

4 a) $(5.2 \times 10^6) + (6.4 \times 10^5) = (5.2 \times 10^6) + (0.64 \times 10^6)$
$= (5.2 + 0.64) \times 10^6 = 5.84 \times 10^6$
[2 marks available — 1 mark for a correct method of adding
the two numbers, 1 mark for the correct answer]

   b) $(9.7 \times 10^{-2}) - (8 \times 10^{-3}) = (9.7 \times 10^{-2}) - (0.8 \times 10^{-2})$
$= (9.7 - 0.8) \times 10^{-2} = 8.9 \times 10^{-2}$
[2 marks available — 1 mark for a correct method of
subtracting the two numbers, 1 mark for the correct answer]

5 a) Saturn *[1 mark]*

   b) $(5.07 \times 10^4) - (1.27 \times 10^4) = (5.07 - 1.27) \times 10^4$ *[1 mark]*
$= 3.8 \times 10^4 = 38\ 000$ km *[1 mark]*
[2 marks available in total — as above]

   c) $(4.88 \times 10^3) + (1.16 \times 10^5)$
$= (0.0488 \times 10^5) + (1.16 \times 10^5)$ *[1 mark]*
$= 1.2088 \times 10^5 = 120\ 880$ km *[1 mark]*
This is less than 140 000 km, so
the diameter of Jupiter is larger. *[1 mark]*
[3 marks available in total — as above]

Answers

Section Two — Algebra

Page 12: Surds

1 a) $\sqrt{7} + 4$ *[1 mark]*
   b) $-2\sqrt{3} + 1 + 4\sqrt{3} - 6 = (-2\sqrt{3} + 4\sqrt{3}) + (1 - 6)$
   $= 2\sqrt{3} - 5$
   [2 marks available — 1 mark for each correct term]

2 Perimeter $= \sqrt{3} + 4\sqrt{2} + 2\sqrt{3} + \sqrt{2}$
   $= (4\sqrt{2} + \sqrt{2}) + (\sqrt{3} + 2\sqrt{3})$
   $= 5\sqrt{2} + 3\sqrt{3}$ cm
   [3 marks available — 1 mark for forming an equation for the perimeter, 1 mark for each correct term]

3 a) $P + Q = \sqrt{5} - \sqrt{7} + \sqrt{5} - 2\sqrt{7}$
   $= 2\sqrt{5} - 3\sqrt{7}$
   [2 marks available — 1 mark for each correct term]
   b) $Q - P = \sqrt{5} - 2\sqrt{7} - (\sqrt{5} - \sqrt{7})$
   $= \sqrt{5} - 2\sqrt{7} - \sqrt{5} + \sqrt{7}$ *[1 mark]*
   $= -\sqrt{7}$ *[1 mark]*
   [2 marks available in total — as above]

Page 13: Expanding Brackets

1 a) $(x + 7)(2x - 2) = 2x^2 - 2x + 14x - 14 = 2x^2 + 12x - 14$
   [2 marks available — 1 mark for expanding the brackets correctly, 1 mark for simplifying]
   b) $(3x - 2)(x - 5) = 3x^2 - 15x - 2x + 10 = 3x^2 - 17x + 10$
   [2 marks available — 1 mark for expanding the brackets correctly, 1 mark for simplifying]

2 a) $(3x + 1)^2 = (3x + 1)(3x + 1) = 9x^2 + 3x + 3x + 1 = 9x^2 + 6x + 1$
   [2 marks available — 1 mark for expanding the brackets correctly, 1 mark for simplifying]
   b) $(4x - 2)^2 = (4x - 2)(4x - 2) = 16x^2 - 8x - 8x + 4$
   $= 16x^2 - 16x + 4$
   [2 marks available — 1 mark for expanding the brackets correctly, 1 mark for simplifying]

3 All sides of a square are equal,
   so area $= (2x + 7)(2x + 7)$ *[1 mark]*
   $= 4x^2 + 14x + 14x + 49$ *[1 mark]*
   $= 4x^2 + 28x + 49$ cm^2 *[1 mark]*
   [3 marks available in total — as above]

Page 14: Factorising

1 a) $5x^2 - 35x = 5(x^2 - 7x)$
   $= 5x(x - 7)$
   [2 marks available — 2 marks for the correct final answer, otherwise 1 mark if the expression is only partially factorised]
   b) $6y + 3xy = 3(2y + xy)$
   $= 3y(2 + x)$
   [2 marks available — 2 marks for the correct final answer, otherwise 1 mark if the expression is only partially factorised]
   c) $xy^2 - x^2y = x(y^2 - xy)$
   $= xy(y - x)$
   [2 marks available — 2 marks for the correct final answer, otherwise 1 mark if the expression is only partially factorised]

2 a) $x^2 - 36 = x^2 - 6^2 = (x + 6)(x - 6)$
   [2 marks available — 2 marks for the correct final answer, otherwise 1 mark for attempting to use the difference of two squares]
   b) $49y^2 - 1 = (7y)^2 - 1^2 = (7y + 1)(7y - 1)$
   [2 marks available — 2 marks for the correct final answer, otherwise 1 mark for attempting to use the difference of two squares]
   c) $16r^2 - 81s^2 = (4r)^2 - (9s)^2 = (4r + 9s)(4r - 9s)$
   [2 marks available — 2 marks for the correct final answer, otherwise 1 mark for attempting to use the difference of two squares]

Pages 15-16: Solving Equations

1 a) $6(x - 2) = -3(x - 5)$
   $6x - 12 = -3x + 15$ *[1 mark]*
   $9x = 27$ *[1 mark]*
   $x = 3$ *[1 mark]*
   [3 marks available in total — as above]
   b) $4(3y - 2) = 2(2y - 3)$
   $12y - 8 = 4y - 6$ *[1 mark]*
   $8y = 2$ *[1 mark]*
   $y = \frac{1}{4}$ *[1 mark]*
   [3 marks available in total — as above]

2 a) $a^2 = 49$
   $a = \pm\sqrt{49}$
   $a = \pm 7$
   [2 marks available — 1 mark for each correct answer]
   b) $4b^2 = 64$
   $b^2 = 16$
   $b = \pm\sqrt{16}$
   $b = \pm 4$
   [2 marks available — 1 mark for each correct answer, or 1 mark for a correct method with no correct answers]
   c) $c^2 + 19 = 100$
   $c^2 = 81$
   $c = \pm\sqrt{81}$
   $c = \pm 9$
   [2 marks available — 1 mark for each correct answer, or 1 mark for a correct method with no correct answers]

3 a) $m^2 + 5 = (m - 2)(m + 5)$
   $m^2 + 5 = m^2 + 5m - 2m - 10$
   $m^2 + 5 = m^2 + 3m - 10$
   $3m - 10 = 5$
   $3m = 15$, so $m = 5$
   [3 marks available — 1 mark for expanding the brackets on the RHS, 1 mark for collecting like terms on each side, 1 mark for the correct solution]
   b) $(n + 3)(n + 2) = (n - 3)(n + 6)$
   $n^2 + 5n + 6 = n^2 + 3n - 18$
   $5n - 3n = -18 - 6$
   $2n = -24$ so $n = -12$
   [4 marks available — 1 mark for expanding the brackets on the LHS, 1 mark for expanding the brackets on the RHS, 1 mark for collecting like terms on each side, 1 mark for the correct solution]

4 a) $\frac{2r - 5}{3} = \frac{r + 1}{5}$
   $5(2r - 5) = 3(r + 1)$ *[1 mark]*
   $10r - 25 = 3r + 3$ *[1 mark]*
   $7r = 28$ *[1 mark]*
   $r = 4$ *[1 mark]*
   [4 marks available in total — as above]
   b) $\frac{s - 9}{5} = \sqrt[3]{2s^3 + 6s^3}$
   $\frac{s - 9}{5} = \sqrt[3]{8s^3}$ *[1 mark]*
   $\frac{s - 9}{5} = 2s$ *[1 mark]*
   $s - 9 = 10s$ *[1 mark]*
   $9s = -9$, so $s = -1$ *[1 mark]*
   [4 marks available in total — as above]

Pages 17-18: Equations from Words and Diagrams

1   Call Claire's number x.
    Then Han's number is $3x$ and Kate's number is $x + 8$.
    The numbers sum to 88, so $3x + x + (x + 8) = 88$
    $5x + 8 = 88$, so $5x = 80$ and $x = 16$
    So the number Claire is thinking of is 16.
    [3 marks available — 1 mark for forming expressions for each person's number, 1 mark for forming an equation for the sum of the numbers, 1 mark for solving the equation and stating the correct number for Claire]

2   BC is twice as long as AB, so $BC = 2(2x + 3)$. *[1 mark]*
    Perimeter is 21 cm, so
    $(2x + 3) + 2(2x + 3) + (4x + 2) = 21$ *[1 mark]*
    $2x + 3 + 4x + 6 + 4x + 2 = 21$
    $10x + 11 = 21$
    $10x = 10$ so $x = 1$ *[1 mark]*
    $BC = 2(2 \times 1 + 3) = 10$ cm *[1 mark]*
    [4 marks available in total — as above]

3   Call the number of points Adam scores x. Then Caitlin scores $4x$ points and Maya scores $x - 12$. The total number of points is 78, so
    $4x + x + (x - 12) = 78$
    $6x - 12 = 78$
    $6x = 90$
    $x = 15$
    So Caitlin scores $4 \times 15 = 60$ points, Adam scores 15 points and Maya scores $15 - 12 = 3$ points.
    [4 marks available — 1 mark for forming expressions for the number of points each person scored, 1 mark for forming an equation for the total number of points scored, 1 mark for solving the equation, 1 mark for the correct number of points that each person scored]

4   If Jin spent x, then Lacey spent $4x$ and Leon spent $x - 5$. *[1 mark]*
    The difference between Lacey and Jin is £30, so
    $4x - x = 30$
    $3x = 30$ so $x = 10$ *[1 mark]*
    In total the three friends spent $4x + x + (x - 5) = 6x - 5$ *[1 mark]*
    So they spent $6 \times 10 - 5 = £55$ *[1 mark]*
    [3 marks available in total — as above]

5   Perimeter of the pentagon is $5(3x - 1) = 15x - 5$
    Perimeter of the rectangle is
    $2x + (x + 4) + 2x + (x + 4) = 6x + 8$
    Pentagon's perimeter is double the rectangle's perimeter, so
    $15x - 5 = 2(6x + 8)$
    $15x - 5 = 12x + 16$
    $3x = 21$ so $x = 7$
    The side length of the pentagon is $3 \times 7 - 1 = 20$ cm.
    [4 marks available — 1 mark for forming expressions for the perimeter of the pentagon and the rectangle, 1 mark for forming a correct equation involving both perimeters, 1 mark for solving the equation, 1 mark for finding the side length of the pentagon]

6   Call the smallest number x.
    Middle number is double the smallest number, so is equal to $2x$.
    The largest number is 3 times the sum of the smaller numbers, so is equal to $3(x + 2x) = 9x$.
    The product of the numbers is 18, so
    $x \times 2x \times 9x = 18x^3 = 18$
    $x^3 = 1$ so $x = 1$
    So the smallest number is 1, the middle number is $2 \times 1 = 2$ and the largest number is $9 \times 1 = 9$.
    [4 marks available — 1 mark for forming expressions for the three numbers, 1 mark for forming an equation for the product of the three numbers, 1 mark for solving the equation, 1 mark for finding the correct three numbers]

Page 19: Rearranging Formulas

1   $a - 4 = \dfrac{b - 1}{5}$
    $5(a - 4) = b - 1$
    $5a - 20 = b - 1$ *[1 mark]*
    $b = 5a - 19$ *[1 mark]*
    [2 marks available in total — as above]

2   $K = \dfrac{mv^2}{2}$
    $2K = mv^2$ *[1 mark]*
    $\dfrac{2K}{m} = v^2$ *[1 mark]*
    $v = \pm\sqrt{\dfrac{2K}{m}}$ *[1 mark]*
    [3 marks available in total — as above]

3   $r = s^2 - (t + 2)^2$
    $(t + 2)^2 = s^2 - r$ *[1 mark]*
    $t + 2 = \pm\sqrt{s^2 - r}$ *[1 mark]*
    $t = \pm\sqrt{s^2 - r} - 2$ *[1 mark]*
    [3 marks available in total — as above]

4   $m = \dfrac{1}{n - 2} + 7$
    $m - 7 = \dfrac{1}{n - 2}$ *[1 mark]*
    $(m - 7)(n - 2) = 1$
    $n - 2 = \dfrac{1}{m - 7}$ *[1 mark]*
    $n = \dfrac{1}{m - 7} + 2$ *[1 mark]*
    [3 marks available in total — as above]

Pages 20-21: Sequences

1   a) Multiply the previous term by 4. *[1 mark]*
    b) Geometric *[1 mark]*

2   a) $5 \quad 13 \quad 21 \quad 29$
        $\quad +8 \quad +8 \quad +8$
        The common difference is 8, so $8n$ is in the formula.
        $n = 1 \quad\ \ 2 \quad\ \ 3 \quad\ \ 4$
        $8n = 8 \quad 16 \quad 24 \quad 32$
        $\qquad\quad |-3 \ \ |-3 \ \ |-3 \ \ |-3$
        $n\text{th term} = 5 \quad 13 \quad 21 \quad 29$
        You have to subtract 3 to get to the term.
        So the expression for the nth term is $8n - 3$.
        [2 marks available — 2 marks for the correct expression, otherwise 1 mark for 8n]
    b) If 52 is a term in the sequence, then $8n - 3 = 52$.
        $8n = 55$ so $n = 6.875$ *[1 mark]*
        n is not a whole number, so 52 is not in the sequence and Maddy is incorrect. *[1 mark]*
        [2 marks available in total — as above]
    c) $8n - 3 = 500$
        $8n = 503$ so $n = 62.875$ *[1 mark]*
        So the first number in the sequence that is over 500 will be when $n = 63$. *[1 mark]*
        $(8 \times 63) - 3 = 504 - 3 = 501$ *[1 mark]*
        [3 marks available in total — as above]

3   a) 7th term $= 18 + 29 = 47$ *[1 mark]*
        8th term $= 29 + 47 = 76$ *[1 mark]*
        [2 marks available in total — as above]
    b) 4th term $= 29 - 18 = 11$ *[1 mark]*
        3rd term $= 18 - 11 = 7$ *[1 mark]*
        [2 marks available in total — as above]

4 a) 2 11 26 47

+9 +15 +21

The difference increases by 6.

The next term is 21 + 6 = 27 bigger, so it's 47 + 27 = 74.

The following term is 27 + 6 = 33 bigger,

so it's 74 + 33 = 107, which is odd.

[2 marks available — 1 mark for the correct 5th term, 1 mark for the correct 6th term and conclusion]

b) The nth term is $3n^2 - 1$, so $3n^2 - 1 = 506$. *[1 mark]*

$3n^2 = 507$

$n^2 = 169$ *[1 mark]*

$n = \sqrt{169} = 13$ *[1 mark]*

[3 marks available in total — as above]

n = −13 doesn't make sense when it comes to sequences.

Pages 22-23: Inequalities

1 a) $6a < 78$

$a < 78 \div 6$

$a < 13$ *[1 mark]*

b) $3b + 4 \geq 54 - 2b$

$3b + 2b \geq 54 - 4$

$5b \geq 50$ *[1 mark]*

$b \geq 50 \div 5$

$b \geq 10$ *[1 mark]*

[2 marks available in total — as above]

c) $2c - 4 \leq 5c + 17$

$2c - 5c \leq 17 + 4$

$-3c \leq 21$ (or $3c \geq -21$) *[1 mark]*

$c \geq 21 \div -3$ (or $c \geq -21 \div 3$)

$c \geq -7$ *[1 mark]*

[2 marks available in total — as above]

2 a) $\dfrac{11 - 2x}{3} \geq x - 3$

$11 - 2x \geq 3(x - 3)$

$11 - 2x \geq 3x - 9$ *[1 mark]*

$-2x - 3x \geq -9 - 11$

$-5x \geq -20$ (or $5x \leq 20$) *[1 mark]*

$x \leq -20 \div -5$ (or $x \leq 20 \div 5$)

$x \leq 4$ *[1 mark]*

[3 marks available in total — as above]

b) 1, 2, 3 or 4 *[1 mark]*

3 a) Perimeter of hexagon = $6 \times (3x + 1) = 18x + 6$ *[1 mark]*

The perimeter of the hexagon is less than or equal to 114 cm, so $18x + 6 \leq 114$ *[1 mark]*

[2 marks available in total — as above]

b) $18x + 6 \leq 114$

$18x \leq 108$ *[1 mark]*

$x \leq 108 \div 18$

$x \leq 6$ *[1 mark]*

$x > 5$ and $x \leq 6$, so $x = 6$ and the hexagon has a side length of $3x + 1 = 3 \times 6 + 1 = 19$ cm *[1 mark]*

[3 marks available in total — as above]

4 a) $7x + 10 > 9x$ *[1 mark]*

b) (i) $7x + 10 > 9x$

$7x - 9x > -10$

$-2x > -10$

$x < -10 \div -2$

$x < 5$

[2 marks available — 1 mark for attempting to solve an inequality, 1 mark for correctly solving the inequality]

(ii) If $x < 5$, then $x = 4$ is x's maximum value *[1 mark]*

So the maximum distance Salim could have cycled is:

$(7 \times 4) + 10 = 38$ km *[1 mark]*

[2 marks available in total — as above]

Pages 24-25: Quadratic Equations

1 1 and 7 multiply to give 7 and add to give 8,

so $x^2 + 8x + 7 = (x + 1)(x + 7)$

[2 marks available — 1 mark for correct numbers in brackets, 1 mark for correct signs]

2 −1 and −4 multiply to give 4 and add to give −5,

so $x^2 - 5x + 4 = (x - 1)(x - 4)$

[2 marks available — 1 mark for correct numbers in brackets, 1 mark for correct signs]

3 He is not correct.

The solutions are the values that make each bracket equal zero, but $6 + 6 = 12$ and $-1 - 1 = -2$.

[2 marks available — 1 mark for stating Sammy is not correct, 1 mark for a correct explanation]

The correct solutions are −6 and 1.

4 a) 1 and −2 multiply to give −2 and add to give −1,

so $x^2 - x - 2 = (x + 1)(x - 2)$

[2 marks available — 1 mark for correct numbers in brackets, 1 mark for correct signs]

b) $x + 1 = 0$ or $x - 2 = 0$

$x = -1$ or $x = 2$

[1 mark for both solutions]

5 2 and 5 multiply to give 10 and add to give 7,

so $x^2 + 7x + 10 = (x + 2)(x + 5)$

[1 mark for correct numbers in brackets, 1 mark for correct signs]

$x + 2 = 0$ or $x + 5 = 0$

$x = -2$ or $x = -5$

[1 mark for both solutions]

[3 marks available in total — as above]

6 $x^2 - x = 42$, so $x^2 - x - 42 = 0$ *[1 mark]*

−7 and 6 multiply to give −42 and add to give −1,

so $x^2 - x - 42 = (x - 7)(x + 6)$

[1 mark for correct numbers in brackets, 1 mark for correct signs]

$x - 7 = 0$ or $x + 6 = 0$

$x = 7$ or $x = -6$

[1 mark for both solutions]

[4 marks available in total — as above]

7 a) Area = $(x + 2)(x - 3)$ *[1 mark]*

= $x^2 - x - 6$ cm^2 *[1 mark]*

[2 marks available in total — as above]

b) $x^2 - x - 6 = 24$ *[1 mark]*

$x^2 - x - 30 = 0$ *[1 mark]*

5 and −6 multiply to give −30 and add to give −1,

so $x^2 - x - 30 = (x + 5)(x - 6)$

[1 mark for correct numbers in brackets, 1 mark for correct signs]

$x + 5 = 0$ or $x - 6 = 0$

$x = -5$ or $x = 6$

x is positive, so $x = 6$ *[1 mark]*

[5 marks available in total — as above]

Pages 26-27: Simultaneous Equations

1    $5x + 3y = 14$ (1)
     $2x + 3y = 11$ (2)
     (1) − (2):
     $5x + 3y = 14$
     $-\underline{2x + 3y = 11}$ $2x + 3y = 11$
     $3x = 3$ $2 + 3y = 11$
     $x = 1$ *[1 mark]* $y = 3$ *[1 mark]*
     [2 marks available in total — as above]

2    $2x + 4y = 12$ (1) $\xrightarrow{\times 2}$ $4x + 8y = 24$ (3) *[1 mark]*
     $4x + 5y = 18$ (2)
     (3) − (2):
     $4x + 8y = 24$
     $-\underline{4x + 5y = 18}$ $2x + 4y = 12$
     $3y = 6$ $2x + 8 = 12$
     $y = 2$ *[1 mark]* $x = 2$ *[1 mark]*
     [3 marks available in total — as above]

3    $3x − 8y = 7$ (1)
     $2x − 2y = 8$ (2) $\xrightarrow{\times 4}$ $8x − 8y = 32$ (3) *[1 mark]*
     (3) − (1):
     $8x − 8y = 32$
     $-\underline{3x − 8y = 7}$ $2x − 2y = 8$
     $5x = 25$ $10 − 2y = 8$
     $x = 5$ *[1 mark]* $y = 1$ *[1 mark]*
     [3 marks available in total — as above]

4    $2x + 3y = 16$ (1) $\xrightarrow{\times 2}$ $4x + 6y = 32$ (3) *[1 mark]*
     $3x + 2y = 14$ (2) $\xrightarrow{\times 3}$ $9x + 6y = 42$ (4) *[1 mark]*
     (4) − (3):
     $9x + 6y = 42$
     $-\underline{4x + 6y = 32}$ $2x + 3y = 16$
     $5x = 10$ $4 + 3y = 16$
     $x = 2$ *[1 mark]* $y = 4$ *[1 mark]*
     [4 marks available in total — as above]

5    $3x − 5y = −1$ (1) $\xrightarrow{\times 5}$ $15x − 25y = −5$ (3) *[1 mark]*
     $5x + 6y = −16$ (2) $\xrightarrow{\times 3}$ $15x + 18y = −48$ (4) *[1 mark]*
     (3) − (4):
     $15x − 25y = −5$
     $-\underline{15x + 18y = −48}$ $3x − 5y = −1$
     $−43y = 43$ $3x + 5 = −1$
     $y = −1$ *[1 mark]* $x = −2$ *[1 mark]*
     [4 marks available in total — as above]

6   Difference between ages is 8, so $y − x = 8$ *[1 mark]*
     Sum of ages is 56, so $x + y = 56$ *[1 mark]*
     $y − x = 8$ (1)
     $x + y = 56$ (2)
     (1) + (2):
     $y − x = 8$
     $+\underline{x + y = 56}$ $y − x = 8$
     $2y = 64$ $32 − x = 8$
     $y = 32$ *[1 mark]* $x = 24$ *[1 mark]*
     So Amar is 24 and Carla is 32.
     [4 marks available in total — as above]

7   From Linus's score: $4x + y = 17$ *[1 mark]*
     From Selma's score: $2x + 3y = 21$ *[1 mark]*
     $4x + y = 17$ (1)
     $2x + 3y = 21$ (2) $\xrightarrow{\times 2}$ $4x + 6y = 42$ (3) *[1 mark]*
     (3) − (1):
     $4x + 6y = 42$
     $-\underline{4x + y = 17}$ $4x + y = 17$
     $5y = 25$ $4x + 5 = 17$
     $y = 5$ *[1 mark]* $x = 3$ *[1 mark]*
     So a spade is worth 3 points and a diamond is worth 5 points.
     [5 marks available in total — as above]

Pages 28-29: Proof

1   a)   E.g. $9 + 9 = 18$, which is not a multiple of 4. *[1 mark]*
     b)   E.g. $−1 − (−2) = 1$ and $−1 + (−2) = −3$. *[1 mark]*

2   LHS: $(n + 5)(2n − 4) + 2 = 2n^2 − 4n + 10n − 20 + 2$ *[1 mark]*
     $ = 2n^2 + 6n − 18$ *[1 mark]*
     $ = 2(n^2 + 3n − 9) =$ RHS *[1 mark]*
     [3 marks available in total — as above]

3    $4(2r + 3) + 7(r − 1) = 8r + 12 + 7r − 7$
     $ = 15r + 5$
     $ = 5(3r + 1)$
     $4(2r + 3) + 7(r − 1)$ can be written as $5 \times$ a whole number
     (where the whole number is $(3r + 1)$), so it is a multiple of 5.
     *[3 marks available — 1 mark for expanding brackets and
     simplifying, 1 mark for writing the expression as 5(3r + 1),
     1 mark for explaining why this is a multiple of 5]*

4   LHS: $x(5x + 2) + 2(3x + 8) − 4x^2 = 5x^2 + 2x + 6x + 16 − 4x^2$
     $ = x^2 + 8x + 16$
     4 and 4 multiply to give 16 and add to give 8,
     so $x^2 + 8x + 16 = (x + 4)(x + 4) = (x + 4)^2 =$ RHS
     *[3 marks available — 1 mark for expanding LHS,
     1 mark for collecting terms, 1 mark for factorising]*

5   Area of rectangle $= xy$
     If length and width are doubled then the new length is $2x$
     and the new width is $2y$.
     The area of the new rectangle $= 2x \times 2y = 4xy$.
     $4xy = 4 \times (xy) = 4 \times$ (original area), so the new area
     is four times larger than the original area.
     *[3 marks available — 1 mark for finding the area of original
     rectangle, 1 mark for finding the new length and width, 1 mark
     for finding the area of the new rectangle]*

6   E.g. Call an integer x.
     x, $x + 1$ and $x + 2$ are three consecutive integers.
     $x + (x + 1) + (x + 2) = 3x + 3 = 3(x + 1)$
     Their sum can be written as $3 \times$ a whole number (where the whole
     number is $(x + 1)$), so it is a multiple of 3.
     *[4 marks available — 1 mark for forming expressions for 3
     consecutive integers, 1 mark for forming an expression for their
     sum, 1 mark for writing the expression as 3 × n (where n is an
     integer), 1 mark for explaining why this is a multiple of 3]*

7   LHS: $2(ax + 2) − 3b + 4ax = 2ax + 4 − 3b + 4ax = 6ax + (4 − 3b)$
     If identity is true, then $6ax + (4 − 3b) \equiv 18x + 1$
     Comparing x coefficients: $6a = 18$, so $a = 3$
     Comparing constants: $4 − 3b = 1$, so $b = 1$
     *[5 marks available — 1 mark for expanding the LHS and
     collecting like terms, 1 mark for comparing x coefficients,
     1 mark for finding a, 1 mark for comparing constants,
     1 mark for finding b]*

Answers

Section Three — Graphs

Pages 30-31: Parallel Lines

1. $3y = 6x + 12 \Rightarrow y = 2x + 4$
   So $3y = 6x + 12$ *[1 mark]* and $y = 2x - 2$ *[1 mark]*
   E.g. The graphs of these equations are both straight lines with a gradient of 2, so they are parallel. *[1 mark]*
   [3 marks available in total — as above]
   $y = -2x$ has a gradient of -2, and $y = 2x^2$ is not a straight line.

2. $y = 7x - 5$ has a gradient of 7
   a) $y = 7x$ *[1 mark]*
   b) $y = \text{m}x + \text{c} = 7x + \text{c}$
      When $x = 1$, $y = 6$
      $6 = (7 \times 1) + \text{c} \Rightarrow \text{c} = -1$
      So $y = 7x - 1$
      [3 marks available — 1 mark for using m = 7, 1 mark for finding c = –1, 1 mark for the correct answer]

3. The lines are parallel so they have the same gradient:
   Gradient of **L** $= \dfrac{\text{change in } y}{\text{change in } x} = \dfrac{0-6}{3-0} = \dfrac{-6}{3} = -2$
   So $y = -2x + \text{c}$
   When $x = -3$, $y = 7$
   $7 = (-2 \times -3) + \text{c} \Rightarrow 7 = 6 + \text{c} \Rightarrow \text{c} = 1$
   So the y-intercept is 1.
   [3 marks available — 1 mark for a correct method of finding the gradient, 1 mark for the correct gradient, 1 mark for finding the y-intercept]

4. $2y + 8x = 4 \Rightarrow 2y = -8x + 4 \Rightarrow y = -4x + 2$
   $8x - 2y = 4 \Rightarrow 2y = 8x - 4 \Rightarrow y = 4x - 2$
   So $2y + 8x = 4$ has a gradient of -4 and $8x - 2y = 4$ has a gradient of 4. The gradients are different so the lines are not parallel.
   [3 marks available — 1 mark for the correct gradient of 2y + 8x = 4, 1 mark for the correct gradient of 8x – 2y = 4, 1 mark for the correct answer with an explanation]

5. $2x - 3y - 4 = 0 \Rightarrow 3y = 2x - 4 \Rightarrow y = \dfrac{2}{3}x - \dfrac{4}{3}$
   The gradient is m $= \dfrac{2}{3}$, so $y = \text{m}x + \text{c} = \dfrac{2}{3}x + \text{c}$
   When $x = 6$, $y = 1$, so $1 = (\dfrac{2}{3} \times 6) + \text{c} \Rightarrow \text{c} = -3$
   So the equation of the parallel line is $y = \dfrac{2}{3}x - 3$
   [4 marks available — 1 mark for finding gradient = 2/3, 1 mark for correctly using x = 6 and y = 1, 1 mark for finding c = –3, 1 mark for the correct answer]

6. a) Line **M**: $y + 3x = 3 \Rightarrow y = -3x + 3$ *[1 mark]*
      Line **N**: $3y - Ax = 3 \Rightarrow 3y = Ax + 3 \Rightarrow y = \dfrac{A}{3}x + 1$ *[1 mark]*
      The lines are parallel, so the gradients are the same:
      $-3 = \dfrac{A}{3} \Rightarrow A = -3 \times 3 = -9$ *[1 mark]*
      [3 marks available in total — as above]
   b) E.g. No, he's incorrect. Line M has a y-intercept of 3 and line N has a y-intercept of 1, so line M is above line N at $x = 0$. They're parallel, so line M is always above line N. *[1 mark]*

Pages 32-33: Straight Line Graphs

1. Gradient $= \dfrac{6 - -2}{4 - 0} = \dfrac{8}{4} = 2$
   So $y = 2x + \text{c}$
   When $x = 0$, $y = -2$
   $-2 = (2 \times 0) + \text{c} \Rightarrow \text{c} = -2$
   So $y = 2x - 2$
   [4 marks available — 1 mark for a correct method for finding the gradient, 1 mark for the correct gradient, 1 mark for putting one point into the equation, 1 mark for the correct answer]

2. Gradient $= \dfrac{1 - 4}{2 - 1} = \dfrac{-3}{1} = -3$
   So $y = -3x + \text{c}$
   When $x = 1$, $y = 4$
   $4 = (-3 \times 1) + \text{c} \Rightarrow \text{c} = 7$
   So $y = -3x + 7$
   [4 marks available — 1 mark for a correct method for finding the gradient, 1 mark for the correct gradient, 1 mark for putting one point into the equation, 1 mark for the correct answer]

3. a) Gradient $= \dfrac{4 - 0}{5 - -3} = \dfrac{4}{8} = \dfrac{1}{2}$
      So $y = \dfrac{1}{2}x + \text{c}$
      When $x = -3$, $y = 0$
      $0 = (\dfrac{1}{2} \times -3) + \text{c} \Rightarrow \text{c} = \dfrac{3}{2}$
      So $y = \dfrac{1}{2}x + \dfrac{3}{2}$
      [4 marks available — 1 mark for a correct method for finding the gradient, 1 mark for the correct gradient, 1 mark for putting one point into the equation, 1 mark for the correct answer]
   b) E.g. When $x = -1$, $y = (\dfrac{1}{2} \times -1) + \dfrac{3}{2} = 1$, so $(-1, 1)$ is on the line, which means $(-1, 2)$ lies above the line. *[1 mark]*

4. a) A: $(-6, -4)$ *[1 mark]* C: $(2, 4)$ *[1 mark]*
      [2 marks available in total — as above]
   b) Gradient $= \dfrac{-4 - 4}{-6 - 2} = \dfrac{-8}{-8} = 1$
      So $y = x + \text{c}$
      When $x = 2$, $y = 4$
      $4 = (2 \times 1) + \text{c} \Rightarrow \text{c} = 2$
      So $y = x + 2$
      [4 marks available — 1 mark for a correct method for finding the gradient, 1 mark for the correct gradient, 1 mark for putting one point into the equation, 1 mark for the correct answer]
   c) E.g. ABC — as $(0, 1)$ lines below the line $y = x + 2$, which contains the side AC of the triangle. *[1 mark]*

5. a) M has coordinates $(\dfrac{1+3}{2}, \dfrac{1+5}{2})$ *[1 mark]* $= (2, 3)$ *[1 mark]*
      [2 marks available in total — as above]
   b) Gradient $= \dfrac{3 - 5}{2 - 1} = \dfrac{-2}{1} = -2$
      So $y = -2x + \text{c}$
      When $x = 1$, $y = 5$
      $5 = (-2 \times 1) + \text{c} \Rightarrow \text{c} = 7$
      So $y = -2x + 7$
      [4 marks available — 1 mark for a correct method for finding the gradient, 1 mark for the correct gradient, 1 mark for putting one point into the equation, 1 mark for the correct answer]
      If you got part a) wrong, you'd still get a mark for putting one point into your equation (provided that you did it correctly).

Answers

Pages 34-35: Quadratic Graphs

1 (5, 2) *[1 mark]*
   *The graph has the same y-value at x = 4 and x = 6, so
   you know the turning point is halfway between at x = 5.*

2 a)

x	−1	0	1	2	3
y	−2	1	2	1	−2

   *[2 marks available — 2 marks for all values correct,
   otherwise 1 mark for two correct values]*

   b)

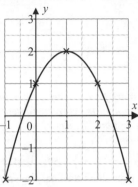

   *[2 marks available — 1 mark if all points are
   plotted correctly, 1 mark for a smooth curve
   joining the correctly plotted points]*

   c) (1, 2) *[1 mark]*

3 The graph has the same y-value at $x = -2$ and $x = 1$.
   The x-coordinate of the turning point is: $\frac{-2+1}{2} = \frac{-1}{2} = -0.5$
   The y-coordinate of the turning point is:
   $y = (-0.5)^2 + (-0.5) - 2 = 0.25 - 0.5 - 2 = -2.25$
   So the turning point has coordinates (−0.5, −2.25).
   *[4 marks available — 1 mark for a correct method for finding
   the x-coordinate, 1 mark for the correct x-coordinate,
   1 mark for a correct method for finding the y-coordinate,
   1 mark for the correct y-coordinate]*

4 a)

x	0	1	2	3	4	5
y	4	0	−2	−2	0	4

   *[2 marks available — 2 marks for all values correct,
   otherwise 1 mark for two correct values]*

   b)

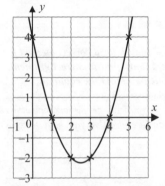

   *[2 marks available — 1 mark if all points are
   plotted correctly, 1 mark for a smooth curve
   joining the correctly plotted points]*

   c) The graph has the same y-value at $x = 1$ and $x = 4$.
   The x-coordinate of the turning point is: $\frac{1+4}{2} = \frac{5}{2} = 2.5$
   The y-coordinate of the turning point is:
   $y = (2.5)^2 - (5 \times 2.5) + 4 = 6.25 - 12.5 + 4 = -2.25$
   So the turning point has coordinates (2.5, −2.25).
   *[4 marks available — 1 mark for a correct method
   for finding the x-coordinate, 1 mark for the correct
   x-coordinate, 1 mark for a correct method for finding
   the y-coordinate, 1 mark for the correct y-coordinate]*

5 a)

x	−3	−2	−1	0	1
y	1	3	3	1	−3

   *[2 marks available — 2 marks for all values correct,
   otherwise 1 mark for at least two correct values]*

   b)

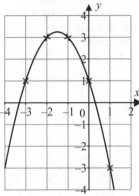

   *[2 marks available — 1 mark if all points are
   plotted correctly, 1 mark for a smooth curve
   joining the correctly plotted points]*

   c) The graph has the same y-value at $x = -3$ and $x = 0$.
   The x-coordinate of the turning point is: $\frac{-3+0}{2} = -1.5$
   The y-coordinate of the turning point is:
   $y = 1 - (3 \times -1.5) - (-1.5)^2 = 1 + 4.5 - 2.25 = 3.25$
   So the turning point has coordinates (−1.5, 3.25).
   *[4 marks available — 1 mark for a correct method
   for finding the x-coordinate, 1 mark for the correct
   x-coordinate, 1 mark for a correct method for finding
   the y-coordinate, 1 mark for the correct y-coordinate]*

Pages 36-37: Harder Graphs

1 **B** *[1 mark]*

2 a)

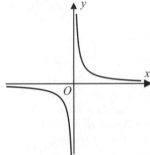

   *[2 marks available — 2 marks for the correct shape,
   lose 1 mark for any intersection with the axes]*

   b)

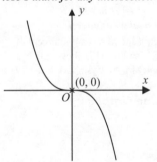

   *[2 marks available — 1 mark for the correct shape,
   1 mark for labelling (0, 0)]*

3 $y = -x^3 + 12$ *[1 mark]*
   *The shape of the graph tells you the equation has a $-x^3$ term.
   Put in x = 0 to check you've got the right one: $y = -(0)^3 + 12 = 12$.*

4 a)

x	−2	−1	0	1	2
y	−4	3	4	5	12

[2 marks available — 2 marks for all values correct, otherwise 1 mark for two correct values]

b)

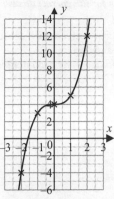

[2 marks available — 1 mark if all points are plotted correctly, 1 mark for a smooth curve joining the correctly plotted points]

5 a)

x	−2	−1	0	1	2
y	−15	−8	−7	−6	1

[2 marks available — 2 marks for all values correct, otherwise 1 mark for two correct values]

b)

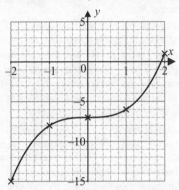

[2 marks available — 1 mark if all points are plotted correctly, 1 mark for a smooth curve joining the correctly plotted points]

Pages 38-39: Solving Quadratics Using Graphs

1 a) $x = −1$ and $x = 2$ *[1 mark for both correct]*

 b) $x = 0$ and $x = 1$ *[1 mark for both correct]*

Don't forget, you can check an exact solution by putting the x-value into the equation and seeing if you get the correct y-value back out.

2 a) $x = −1$ and $x = 4$ *[1 mark for both correct]*

 b) $x = −2.25$ (allow −2.3 to −2.2)
 $x = 5.25$ (allow 5.2 to 5.3)
 [2 marks available — 2 marks for two correct solutions, otherwise 1 mark for one correct solution, or the intersections of the x-axis and the curve drawn]

3 a) 9 *[1 mark]*

 b) $x = −0.5$ (allow −0.6 to −0.4)
 $x = 2.5$ (allow 2.4 to 2.6)
 [2 marks available — 2 marks for two correct solutions, otherwise 1 mark for one correct solution, or the line y = 5 drawn, or the intersections of the line y = 5 and the curve drawn]

4 a)

x	−2	−1	0	1	2	3	4
y	4	−1	−4	−5	−4	−1	4

[2 marks available — 2 marks for all values correct, otherwise 1 mark for at least two correct values]

b)

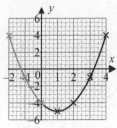

[2 marks available — 1 mark if all points are plotted correctly, 1 mark for a smooth curve joining the correctly plotted points]

 c) $x = −1.5$ (allow −1.6 to −1.4)
 $x = 3.5$ (allow 3.4 to 3.6)
 [2 marks available — 2 marks for two correct solutions, otherwise 1 mark for one correct solution, or the line y = 1 drawn, or the intersections of the line y = 1 and the curve drawn]

5 E.g. Yes, he's correct. The line $y = 8$ intersects the curve at approximately $x = 2.75 = 3$ to the nearest whole number.
[2 marks available — 1 mark for the correct answer, 1 mark for a correct explanation]

6 a) $c = 8$
 [2 marks available — 2 marks for the correct answer, otherwise 1 mark for either of the lines x = −5 or x = −1 drawn, or the intersection of the curve with either of the lines x = −5 or x = −1 drawn]

 b) $c = 4$
 [2 marks available — 2 marks for the correct answer, otherwise 1 mark for the point (−3, 4) drawn]

Pages 40-41: Simultaneous Equations and Graphs

1 a) $x = 3, y = 3$ *[1 mark]*

 b) $x = 2, y = 0.5$ *[1 mark]*

2 a)

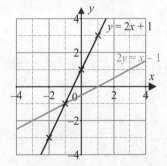

[2 marks available — 2 marks for correctly drawing the line y = 2x + 1, otherwise 1 mark for at least two points plotted correctly]

 b) $x = −1, y = −1$ *[1 mark]*

3 a) $x = 0.5$ *[1 mark]*

   b)

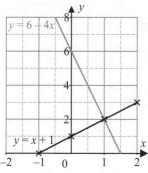

   $x = 1$, $y = 2$
   [3 marks available — 2 marks for correctly drawing the line $y = x + 1$ (otherwise 1 mark for at least two points plotted correctly), 1 mark for the correct solution]

4 a) E.g. The graphs of the equations do not intersect where two grid lines meet. *[1 mark]*

   b) $x = 1$ (allow 1 to 1.2), $y = 2.5$ (allow 2.5 to 2.7) *[1 mark]*
   Use the grid lines nearest to the point of intersection to estimate values for x and y. It's to the right of x = 1 and above y = 2.5, so the exact solution is a little bigger than both.

5

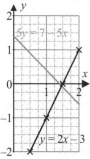

   $x = 1.5$ (allow 1.3 to 1.5), $y = 0$ (allow −0.2 to 0)
   [3 marks available — 2 marks for correctly drawing the line $y = 2x − 3$ (otherwise 1 mark for at least two points plotted correctly), 1 mark for correct values of x and y]
   The point of intersection is to the left of x = 1.5 and below y = 0, so the exact solution is a little smaller than both.

Pages 42-43: Real-Life Graphs

1 **C** *[1 mark]*
   The gradient measures the increase in value. The value is increasing at a constant rate, so the graph is an upwards sloping straight line.

2 a)

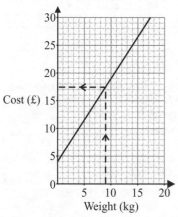

   £17.50 (allow £17.25 to £17.75)
   [2 marks available — 2 marks for a correct answer, otherwise 1 mark for evidence of a correct method]

   b) Rate of increase = gradient = $\dfrac{\text{change in cost}}{\text{change in weight}}$

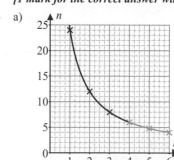

   $= \dfrac{25 - 10}{14 - 4} = \dfrac{15}{10} = £1.50$ per kg
   [2 marks available — 1 mark for a correct method to calculate the gradient, 1 mark for the correct answer (allow £1.40 to £1.60 per kg)]

3 Shape **A**. E.g. The height of the water decreases at a constant rate, so the sides of the sink must be straight.
   [1 mark for the correct answer with a correct explanation]

4 a)

   [2 marks available — 1 mark for three points plotted correctly, 1 mark for a smooth curve joining the correctly plotted points]

   b) 1 hour and 15 minutes (allow ± 10 minutes)
   [2 marks available — 2 marks for a correct answer, otherwise 1 mark for the line $n = 19$ drawn and intersecting the curve]

   c) No, because 9 workers would take approximately 2 hours and 45 minutes which is too long.
   [2 marks available — 1 mark for the line $n = 9$ drawn or the intersection of the line $n = 9$ and the curve drawn or written down, 1 mark for the correct answer]
   You could also go up from 2.5 hours to find that it would take more than 9 people to complete the task in this time.

   d) E.g. Yes, he's correct. *[1 mark]*
   4 workers would take 6 hours, so they would cost $6 × £11 = £66$ each and $4 × £66 = £264$ in total *[1 mark]*
   6 workers would take 4 hours, so they would cost $4 × £11 = £44$ each and $6 × £44 = £264$ in total *[1 mark]*
   [3 marks available in total — as above]
   You'd also get the marks by showing that both 4 and 6 workers will complete the task in the same amount of time (24 hours) and so either group will be paid $24 × £11 = £264$.

Section Four — Ratio and Proportion

Pages 44-45: Ratios

1 $45 ÷ (3 + 4 + 8) = 45 ÷ 15 = 3$ grapes per part
   Sarah: $3 × 3 = 9$ grapes
   Elliot: $3 × 4 = 12$ grapes
   Kai: $3 × 8 = 24$ grapes
   [3 marks available — 1 mark for dividing 45 by the sum of the numbers in the ratio, 1 mark for multiplying this value by each number in the ratio, 1 mark if all three amounts are correct]

2 $96 ÷ (2 + 7 + 3) = 96 ÷ 12 = 8$ cm² per part *[1 mark]*
   Area of rectangle $B = 8 × 7 = 56$ cm² *[1 mark]*
   Length of rectangle $B = 56 ÷ 4 = 14$ cm *[1 mark]*
   [3 marks available in total — as above]

3 Abby can use at most 90 g of salt.
This would be 90 ÷ 8 = 11.25 g per part.
So she can use 11.25 × 3 = 33.75 g of garlic powder and
90 g of salt to make 33.75 + 90 = 123.75 g of the seasoning.
*[3 marks available — 1 mark for 90 ÷ 8 = 11.25, 1 mark for
11.25 × 3 = 33.75, 1 mark for the correct answer]*
*You could try to use all 36 g of garlic powder, but that's
36 ÷ 3 = 12 g per part and would need 12 × 8 = 96 g of salt, which
is more than Abby has. You'd pick up marks for a partially correct
method, but you won't find the correct answer this way.*

4 10 ÷ (3 + 2) = 10 ÷ 5 = 2 games per part *[1 mark]*
So Logan won 2 × 3 = 6 games *[1 mark]*
Gina lost 3 games for every game she won,
so to win 6 games she lost 6 × 3 = 18 games. *[1 mark]*
In total she will have played 6 + 18 = 24 games. *[1 mark]*
[4 marks available in total — as above]

5 Rabia gets 5 parts and Callum gets 2 parts.
So £225 = 5 parts – 2 parts = 3 parts
1 part = £225 ÷ 3 = £75
Hazel: 3 parts = £225
Rabia: 5 parts = £75 × 5 = £375
Callum: 2 parts = £75 × 2 = £150
*[4 marks available — 1 mark for expressing £225 as a
number of parts, 1 mark for finding the value of 1 part,
1 mark for multiplying this value by each number in
the ratio, 1 mark if all three amounts are correct]*

6 The fruit salad is made up of 5 + 4 + 3 = 12 parts,
so contains: $\frac{5}{12}$ bananas, $\frac{4}{12}$ apples and $\frac{3}{12}$ strawberries.
18 kg of fruit salad contains:
$\frac{5}{12}$ × 18 = 7.5 kg of bananas
$\frac{4}{12}$ × 18 = 6 kg of apples
$\frac{3}{12}$ × 18 = 4.5 kg of strawberries
Bananas cost 7.5 × £0.70 = £5.25
Apples cost 6 × £3.10 = £18.60
Strawberries cost 4.5 × £10 = £45
18 kg of fruit salad costs:
£5.25 + £18.60 + £45 = £68.85
*[5 marks available — 1 mark for a correct method for finding
the mass of each fruit, 1 mark for the correct mass of one fruit,
1 mark for the correct masses of the other two fruits, 1 mark
for working out the price for each fruit, 1 mark for the correct
answer]*

Pages 46-48: Direct and Inverse Proportion

1 For 1 portion of soup he would need:
Carrots: 720 g ÷ 15 = 48 g Parsnips: 540 g ÷ 15 = 36 g
Potatoes : 0.9 kg ÷ 15 = 0.06 kg
Chillies: 5 ÷ 15 = $\frac{1}{3}$ of a chilli
For 27 portions of soup he'd need:
Carrots: 48 g × 27 = 1296 g Parsnips: 36 g × 27 = 972 g
Potatoes: 0.06 kg × 27 = 1.62 kg
Chillies: $\frac{1}{3}$ of a chilli × 27 = 9 chillies
*[3 marks available — 1 mark for dividing the quantities
by 15, 1 mark for multiplying the quantities by 27,
1 mark for four correct answers]*

2 8:15 am to 12:00 pm is 3 hours and 45 minutes = 225 minutes
225 ÷ 5 = 45 minutes per car *[1 mark]*
12:45 to 5:15 pm is 4 hours and 30 minutes = 270 minutes
270 ÷ 45 = 6 cars *[1 mark]*
Gary washed a total of 5 + 6 = 11 cars,
so he earned £9 × 11 = £99 *[1 mark]*
[3 marks available in total — as above]

3 a)

*[3 marks available — 1 mark for a straight line, 1 mark for
a line going through the origin, 1 mark for marking two
correct points (one can be the origin)]*

b) 240 = A × 75, so $A = \frac{240}{75} = 3.2$ *[1 mark]*
So f = 3.2g *[1 mark]*
[2 marks available in total — as above]

4 a) C *[1 mark]*
b) It would take 1 builder 170 × 8 = 1360 days *[1 mark]*
So it would take 5 builders 1360 ÷ 5 = 272 days *[1 mark]*
[2 marks available in total — as above]

5 1 waiter takes 8 × 60 = 480 minutes
10 workers take 480 ÷ 10 = 48 minutes, so 10 waiters is too few.
11 workers take 480 ÷ 11 = 43.63... minutes
This is under 45 minutes, so 11 waiters is the smallest number.
*[3 marks available — 1 mark for 8 × 60 = 480, 1 mark for a
correct calculation of the time taken by a number of waiters
(except for 1 or 8 waiters), 1 mark for the correct answer]*
*You would also get the marks for reasoning that Fatima wants
the food served in 45 ÷ 60 = $\frac{3}{4}$ of the time, so would need
$\frac{4}{3}$ as many workers. 8 × $\frac{4}{3}$ = 10.66... ≈ 11 workers.*

6 a) am = K and $a = \frac{K}{m}$
[2 marks available — 1 mark for each correct answer]
b) K = 20 × 6 = 120, so a = 120 ÷ m (and m = 120 ÷ a)

a	8	6	12
m	15	20	10

*[2 marks available — 1 mark for each correct entry, or
1 mark for calculating K = 120 if no entries are correct]*

7 1 person can assemble 12 cars in 9 × 8 = 72 hours *[1 mark]*
1 person can assemble 1 car in 72 ÷ 12 = 6 hours *[1 mark]*
3 people can assemble 1 car in 6 ÷ 3 = 2 hours *[1 mark]*
3 people can assemble 16 cars in 2 × 16 = 32 hours *[1 mark]*
[4 marks available in total — as above]

Pages 49-50: Percentages

1 a) 18% = 0.18
£2.50 × 0.18 = £0.45
£2.50 + £0.45 = £2.95
*[2 marks available — 1 mark for a correct method for finding
the increased price, 1 mark for the correct increased price]*

b) 85% = 0.85, so 340 × 0.85 = 289 new notepads
and 340 – 289 = 51 old notepads were sold.
289 × 2.95 = £852.55
51 × 2.50 = £127.50
So the company made 852.55 + 127.50 = £980.05
*[3 marks available — 1 mark for a correct method for
finding the money made by selling the new notepads, 1 mark
for the correct money made by selling the new or the old
notepads, 1 mark for the correct answer]*

Answers

102

2 a) 820 × 1.4 = £1148, so the stall's profit = £1148 − £650 = £498
35% = 0.35, so 498 × 0.35 = £147.30 would be donated
[3 marks available — 1 mark for correctly finding the stall's profit, 1 mark for a correct method for finding how much would be donated, 1 mark for the correct amount]

b) £336 is 35% of the profit, so profit = (336 ÷ 35) × 100 = £960
So they sold £960 + £650 = £1610 of cupcakes.
1610 ÷ 1.4 = 1150, so they sold 1150 cupcakes.
[3 marks available — 1 mark for a correct method for finding the stall's profit, 1 mark for the correct profit, 1 mark for the correct answer]

3 On Monday, each roll costs £18.24 ÷ 57 = £0.32
On Tuesday, each roll costs £19.88 ÷ 71 = £0.28
The change in price is £0.32 − £0.28 = £0.04
Percentage decrease = $\frac{0.04}{0.32}$ × 100 = 12.5%
[3 marks available — 1 mark for finding the cost of a roll on each day, 1 mark for a correct method to find percentage change, 1 mark for the correct answer]

4 100 − 80 = 20% of home fans are not wearing their team's shirt.
This is 20% of 90% = 0.2 × 90% = 18% of all the fans. *[1 mark]*
100 − 90 = 10% of all the fans are away fans *[1 mark]*
100 − 85 = 15% of away fans are not wearing their team's shirt.
This is 15% of 10% = 0.15 × 10% = 1.5% of all the fans. *[1 mark]*
So the percentage of all fans not wearing their team's shirt is:
18% + 1.5% = 19.5% *[1 mark]*
[4 marks available in total — as above]
You could also find that 90% × 80% = 72% of the fans are home fans wearing their team's shirt and 10% × 85% = 8.5% of the fans are away fans wearing their team's shirt. So 72% + 8.5% = 80.5% of the fans are wearing their teams shirt, so 100% − 80.5% = 19.5% are not.

5 100% − 35% = 65%
Competitors in 1st round × 65% = 260, so
Competitors in 1st round = 260 ÷ 0.65 = 400 *[1 mark]*
So 400 − 176 = 224 competitors are musicians or dancers.
The ratio 1 : 3 means 3 out of 4 = 75%
of these competitors are musicians *[1 mark]*
75% of 224 = 224 × 0.75 = 168 *[1 mark]*
So 168 ÷ 400 × 100 = 42% *[1 mark]* were musicians.
[4 marks available in total — as above]

Pages 51-52: Compound Growth and Decay

1 a) Multiplier = 1 + 0.02 = 1.02
After 4 years he will have: £2400 × (1.02)⁴ = £2597.837...
= £2597.84 (to the nearest penny)
[3 marks available — 1 mark for working out the multiplier, 1 mark for a correct method, 1 mark for the correct answer]

b) After 5 years: £2400 × (1.02)⁵ = 2649.793...
After 6 years: £2400 × (1.02)⁶ = 2702.789...
So it will take 6 years.
[2 marks available — 1 mark for a correct method, 1 mark for the correct answer]

2 a) Using the formula,
121 = (Insects at start) × (1.1)² *[1 mark]*
Insects at start = 121 ÷ 11² *[1 mark]*
= 121 ÷ 1.21 = 100 *[1 mark]*
[3 marks available in total — as above]

b) Insects after 13 weeks = 100 × (1.1)¹³ *[1 mark]*
= 345.227... *[1 mark]*
So there will be 345 insects after 13 weeks. *[1 mark]*
[3 marks available in total — as above]
Check the context of the question to see if your answer should be a whole number — 0.227 of an insect doesn't make sense.

3 a) Multiplier = 1 − 0.18 = 0.82
After 3 years the phone will be worth:
£650 × (0.82)³ = £358.3892
= £358.39 (to the nearest penny)
[3 marks available — 1 mark for working out the multiplier, 1 mark for a correct method, 1 mark for the correct answer]

b) A quarter of £650 = £650 ÷ 4 = £162.50
After 4 years: £650 × (0.82)⁴ = £293.879...
After 5 years: £650 × (0.82)⁵ = £240.980...
After 6 years: £650 × (0.82)⁶ = £197.604...
After 7 years: £650 × (0.82)⁷ = £162.035...
So it will take 7 years.
[3 marks available — 1 mark for finding a quarter of £650, 1 mark for a correct method, 1 mark for the correct answer]

4 Bushberg Ltd:
First year = £899 × 1.02 = £916.98
Second year = £916.98 × 1.03 = £944.4894
Weynell Bank:
First year = £899 × 1.01 = £907.99
Second year = £907.99 × 1.05 = £953.3895
So Stephen would save £953.3895 − £944.4894 = £8.9001
= £8.90 (to the nearest penny) by choosing Bushberg Ltd.
[4 marks available — 1 mark for using a correct method to find the cost of using either company, 1 mark for the correct cost of using Bushberg Ltd, 1 mark for the correct cost of using Weynell Bank, 1 mark for the correct answer]
You'd still get the marks if you first rounded the cost of each loan to the nearest penny and then calculated the difference to be £8.90.

Pages 53-55: Speed, Density and Pressure

1 a) Volume = 32 × 12 × 15 *[1 mark]*
= 5760 cm³ *[1 mark]*
[2 marks available in total — as above]

b) 1 kg = 1000 g, so 2.5 kg = 2500 g *[1 mark]*
Density = mass ÷ volume, so
density = 2500 ÷ 5760 *[1 mark]*
= 0.434... = 0.4 g/cm³ (1 d.p.) *[1 mark]*
[3 marks available in total — as above]

2 a) Area of triangular face = $\frac{1}{2}$ × 4 × 5 = 10 m² *[1 mark]*
Pressure = force ÷ area
= 500 N ÷ 10 m² *[1 mark]*
= 50 N/m² *[1 mark]*
[3 marks available in total — as above]

b) Force = pressure × area
= 6.5 × 10 *[1 mark]*
= 65 N *[1 mark]*
[2 marks available in total — as above]

3 1 hour = 60 minutes, 1 minute = 60 seconds,
So 2.5 hours = 2.5 × 60 × 60 = 9000 seconds *[1 mark]*
1 km = 1000 m
So 45 km = 45 × 1000 = 45 000 m *[1 mark]*
Speed = distance ÷ time
= 45 000 ÷ 9000
= 5 m/s *[1 mark]*
[3 marks available in total — as above]

4 Time = distance ÷ speed
Time for first part = 75 ÷ 50 = 1.5 hours *[1 mark]*
Distance for second part = 2 × 75 km = 150 km, so
time for second part = 150 ÷ 60 = 2.5 hours *[1 mark]*
Time for third part = 10 ÷ 40 = 0.25 hours *[1 mark]*
Total time = 1.5 + 2.5 + 0.25
= 4.25 hours = 4.25 × 60
= 255 minutes *[1 mark]*
[4 marks available in total — as above]

5   1 m = 100 cm
Volume = 3 680 000 ÷ 100 ÷ 100 ÷ 100 = 3.68 m³ *[1 mark]*
Mass = density × volume
      = 2150 × 3.68 *[1 mark]*
      = 7912 kg *[1 mark]*
1 kg = 1000 g, so 7912 kg = 7 912 000 g *[1 mark]*
[4 marks available in total — as above]

6   a)   Mass = density × volume
      Mass of zinc = 7.14 × 50 = 357 g *[1 mark]*
      Mass of tin = 7.26 × 25 = 181.5 g *[1 mark]*
      If the entire mix weighs 717.7 g. then
      mass of copper = 717.7 − 357 − 181.5 = 179.2 g *[1 mark]*
      density of copper = mass ÷ volume
                    = 179.2 ÷ 20 = 8.96 g/cm³ *[1 mark]*
      [4 marks available in total — as above]

    b)   E.g. Copper because, for the same volume, the metal
      with the highest density will have the most mass.
      [2 marks available — 1 mark for copper,
      1 mark for a correct explanation]

7   Pressure = $\dfrac{\text{force}}{\text{surface area}}$
A force 2 times bigger and a surface area 4 times bigger
means the pressure exerted is $\dfrac{2}{4} = \dfrac{1}{2}$ *[1 mark]* as big.
So the pressure is now $\dfrac{1}{2} × 600 = 300$ N/m² *[1 mark]*
[2 marks available in total — as above]

Section Five — Shapes and Area

Pages 56-57: Congruent Triangles

1   a)   A and C *[1 mark]*
    b)   SAS *[1 mark]*
      Two sides and the angle between them match up.

2   Exactly two pairs of triangles are congruent *[1 mark]*

3   a)   Scalene *[1 mark]*
      The triangles are congruent so the side lengths of DEF match
      the side lengths of ABC, and they are all different.
    b)   *DE* is opposite ∠*EFD* and *BC* is opposite ∠*CAB*,
      so length of *DE* = length of *BC* = 15 cm. *[1 mark]*

4
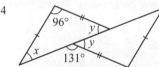

The triangles are congruent, so the two angles
called *y* in the above diagram are equal.
y = 180° − 131° = 49° *[1 mark]* (angles on a straight line)
x = 180° − 96° − 49° = 35° *[1 mark]* (angles in a triangle)
[2 marks available in total — as above]

5   ∠*EFD* = 180° − 84° − 37° = 59°. So *ABC* and *DEF* both have a
side of length 11 cm between angles of 37° and 59°, and so they
are congruent by the AAS condition.
[3 marks available — 1 mark for finding ∠EFD = 59°,
1 mark for stating that ABC and DEF are congruent,
1 mark for a correct explanation]

6   Width of rectangle = 9 + 12 = 21 cm
Area of rectangle = 12 × 21 = 252 cm² *[1 mark]*
Base of triangle = 12 − 7 = 5 cm
Area of triangle = $\dfrac{1}{2}$ × 5 × 12 = 30 cm² *[1 mark]*
Area of region not shaded = 252 − 2 × 30 *[1 mark]*
                        = 192 cm² *[1 mark]*
[4 marks available in total — as above]
You'd get the marks for other correct methods. For example, you
could split the non-shaded region into two trapeziums with areas
$\dfrac{1}{2}$ × (7 + 12) × 12 = 114 cm² and $\dfrac{1}{2}$ × (4 + 9) × 12 = 78 cm²,
with a total area of 114 + 78 = 192 cm².

Pages 58-59: Similar Shapes

1   a)   Scale factor = 6 ÷ 20 = 0.3 *[1 mark]*
      EF = *AB* × 0.3 = 14 × 0.3 = 4.2 cm *[1 mark]*
      [2 marks available in total — as above]
    b)   ∠*EHG* = ∠*ADC* = 106° *[1 mark]*

2   E.g. 180° − 100° − 35° = 45°.
No, the triangles are not similar. The first triangle contains
an angle of 30° but the second triangle does not.
[2 marks available — 1 mark for calculating 45°,
1 mark for the correct answer with an explanation]

3   The perimeters have the same ratio as the side lengths.
3 parts = perimeter of A = 12 cm, so 1 part = 12 cm ÷ 3 = 4 cm
Perimeter of B = 7 parts = 4 cm × 7 = 28 cm
[2 marks available — 1 mark for a correct method,
1 mark for the correct answer]
You could also find side length of A = 12 ÷ 5 = 2.4 cm, so side length of
B = (2.4 ÷ 3) × 7 = 5.6 cm, then perimeter of B is 5.6 cm × 5 = 28 cm
— but this is quite tricky without a calculator.

4   a)   Scale factor = *AE* ÷ *BD* = 8 ÷ 6 = $\dfrac{4}{3}$ *[1 mark]*
      So *EC* = *DC* × $\dfrac{4}{3}$ = 12 × $\dfrac{4}{3}$ = 16 cm *[1 mark]*
      [2 marks available in total — as above]
    b)   E.g. Yes, he's correct. Angles *AED* and *BDC* have the same size
      as the triangles are similar, so sides *AE* and *BD* are parallel.
      [2 marks available — 1 mark for the correct answer,
      1 mark for a correct explanation]

5   *AF* = 864 ÷ 36 = 24 cm *[1 mark]*
Scale factor = *AC* ÷ *AF* = 36 ÷ 24 = 1.5 *[1 mark]*
AB = *AF* ÷ 1.5 = 24 cm ÷ 1.5 = 16 cm *[1 mark]*
Area of *ABEF* = *AF* × *AB* = 24 cm × 16 cm
                  = 384 cm² *[1 mark]*
[4 marks available in total — as above]
You could also work out that the scale factor for the area is
1.5 × 1.5 = 2.25. So area of ABEF = 864 ÷ 2.25 = 384 cm².

6   Scale factor = 19.2 ÷ 24 = 0.8
Height of small triangle = 7 cm × 0.8 = 5.6 cm
Base of shaded region = 24 − 19.2 = 4.8 cm
Hypotenuse of large triangle
    = 20 cm ÷ 0.8 = 25 cm
Sloped side of shaded region
    = 25 − 20 cm = 5 cm
Perimeter of shaded region
    = 7 + 5 + 5.6 + 4.8 = 22.4 cm

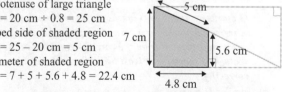

[5 marks available — 1 mark for calculating the scale factor,
1 mark for each correct side length of the shaded region (5 cm,
5.6 cm and 4.8 cm, but not 7 cm), 1 mark for the correct answer]
You could also use Pythagoras' theorem to find the missing lengths,
but it's much simpler to use scale factors.

Pages 60-61: Enlargements

1 An enlargement with a scale factor of 2 and centre (7, 9).
[3 marks available — 1 mark for using either of the words 'enlargement' or 'enlarge', 1 mark for the correct scale factor, 1 mark for the correct centre]

2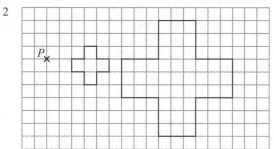

[3 marks available — 3 marks for a correct enlargement, otherwise 2 marks for a correct shape in the wrong position, or an enlargement from the correct centre but of the wrong scale, or 1 mark for at least two sides or three points drawn correctly]

3 a) R (1, 9) *[1 mark]*

   b) Scale factor: 4 *[1 mark]*
      Center: (9, 9) *[1 mark]*
      [2 marks available in total — as above]

4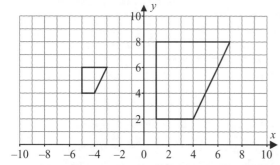

[3 marks available — 3 marks for a correct enlargement, otherwise 2 marks for a correct shape in the wrong position, or an enlargement from the correct centre but of the wrong scale, or 1 mark for at least two sides or three points drawn correctly]

5 a)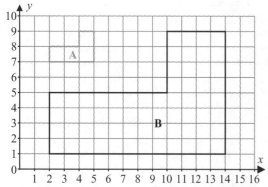

[3 marks available — 3 marks for a correct enlargement, otherwise 2 marks for a correct shape in the wrong position, or an enlargement from the correct centre but of the wrong scale, or 1 mark for at least two sides or three points drawn correctly]

   b) similar *[1 mark]*
      Enlargements have matching angles and proportional sides.

Pages 62-63: Perimeter and Area — Circles

1 Area of outer circle $= \pi \times 10^2 = 100\pi$ cm^2
   Area of two semicircles = area of circle of radius 8 cm
   $\qquad\qquad = \pi \times 8^2 = 64\pi$ cm^2
   Area of shaded region $= 100\pi - 64\pi = 36\pi$
   $\qquad\qquad\qquad = 113.097... = 113.10$ cm^2 (2 d.p.)
   [3 marks available — 1 mark for a correct method for finding the area of a circle, 1 mark for a correct method for finding the area of the shaded region, 1 mark for the correct answer]

2 Arc length of quarter circle $= \frac{1}{4} \times 2\pi \times 6 = 3\pi$ cm *[1 mark]*
   Perimeter of shaded region $= 3\pi + 6 + 6 + 3\pi + 6 + 6$ *[1 mark]*
   $\qquad\qquad = 6\pi + 24 = 42.849...$
   $\qquad\qquad = 42.85$ cm (2 d.p.) *[1 mark]*
   [3 marks available in total — as above]
   You could have added the arc length of one semicircle instead of the arc lengths of two quarter circles.

3 Area of sector $= \frac{30}{360} \times \pi \times 6^2$ *[1 mark]*
   $\qquad = \frac{30 \times 36}{360} \times \pi = \frac{30}{10} \times \pi$
   $\qquad = 3\pi$ cm^2 *[1 mark]*
   [2 marks available in total — as above]

4 a) Arc length $= \frac{140}{360} \times 2\pi \times 7$ *[1 mark]* $= 17.104...$
      $\qquad = 17.10$ cm (2 d.p.) *[1 mark]*
      [2 marks available in total — as above]

   b) Perimeter $= 17.10... + 7 + 7 = 31.10$ cm (2 d.p.) *[1 mark]*

5 Area of large sector $= \frac{35}{360} \times \pi \times 8^2 = 19.547...$
   Area of small sector $= \frac{35}{360} \times \pi \times 5^2 = 7.635...$
   Area of shaded region $= 19.547... - 7.635...$
   $\qquad\qquad = 11.911... = 11.91$ cm^2 (2 d.p.)
   [4 marks available — 1 mark for a correct method for finding the area of a sector, 1 mark for the correct area of either sector, 1 mark for subtracting the smaller area from the larger area, 1 mark for the correct answer]

6 Arc length $= \frac{x}{360} \times 2\pi \times 9 = 2\pi$
   $\Rightarrow x = 360 \div 9 = 40°$
   [3 marks available — 1 mark for writing a correct equation for x, 1 mark for a correct method to solve the equation, 1 mark for the correct answer]

Pages 64-65: Surface Area

1 Surface area $= 4\pi r = 4\pi \times 6^2$ *[1 mark]* $= 452.389...$
   $\qquad\qquad = 450$ cm^2 (2 s.f.) *[1 mark]*
   [2 marks available in total — as above]

2 a) E.g. Surface area $= (2\pi \times 2.1 \times 5.2) + (2\pi \times 2.1^2)$
      $\qquad\qquad \approx (2 \times 3 \times 2 \times 5) + (2 \times 3 \times 2^2)$ *[1 mark]*
      $\qquad\qquad = 60 + 24 = 84$ cm^2 *[1 mark]*
      [2 marks available in total — as above]

   b) Eg. The actual surface area is bigger, as the numbers used in the estimate are all rounded down. *[1 mark]*

3 Side length of cube $= \sqrt[3]{8} = 2$ cm *[1 mark]*
   Area of one face $= 2 \times 2 = 4$ cm^2 *[1 mark]*
   18 faces of the cubes are on the surface of the shape,
   so the total surface area is 4 cm$^2 \times 18 = 72$ cm^2 *[1 mark]*.
   [3 marks available in total — as above]

4 a) Area of base $= 4.1^2 = 16.81$ cm^2 *[1 mark]*
      Area of triangular face $= \frac{1}{2} \times 4.1 \times 2.8 = 5.74$ cm^2 *[1 mark]*
      Surface area $= 16.81 + 5.74 \times 4$ *[1 mark]*
      $\qquad\qquad = 39.77$ cm^2 *[1 mark]*
      [4 marks available in total — as above]

   b) The difference in the surface area of the combined shape and the two separate models is just the area of their square bases:
      $2 \times 4.12^2 = 2 \times 16.81 = 33.62$ cm^2 *[1 mark]*

5 a) Surface area $= \pi r l + \pi r^2 = (\pi \times 5 \times 13) + (\pi \times 5^2)$ *[1 mark]*
      $= 65\pi + 25\pi = 90\pi$ cm^2 *[1 mark]*
   [2 marks available in total — as above]

b) The new face of each piece is a triangle with area
$\frac{1}{2} \times 10 \times 12 = 60$ cm^2 *[1 mark]*. So the total surface area
has increased by $60 \times 2 = 120$ cm^2. *[1 mark]*
[2 marks available in total — as above]

Pages 66-67: Volumes

1   Volume $= \frac{1}{3} \times$ base area $\times$ height $= \frac{1}{3} \times 6^2 \times 5$ *[1 mark]*
     $= \frac{1}{3} \times 36 \times 5 = 12 \times 5 = 60$ cm^3 *[1 mark]*
  [2 marks available in total — as above]

2   Area of triangular face $= \frac{1}{2} \times 8 \times 6 = 24$ cm^2 *[1 mark]*
  Volume of prism = cross-section area $\times$ length $= 24 \times L$ *[1 mark]*
  So $24L = 624 \Rightarrow L = 624 \div 24 = 26$ cm *[1 mark]*
  [3 marks available in total — as above]

3   Volume of prism $= (\frac{1}{2} \times 6 \times 5) \times 8\pi$ *[1 mark]*
      $= 120\pi$ cm^3 *[1 mark]*
  Volume of cone $= \frac{1}{3} \times \pi \times 4^2 \times 9$ *[1 mark]*
      $= 48\pi$ cm^3 *[1 mark]*
  Ratio of volumes $= 120\pi : 48\pi = 5 : 2$ *[1 mark]*
  [5 marks available in total — as above]
  You'd also get the marks if you wrote the two formulas
  in a ratio and then cancelled down to find the answer.

4 a) Volume of sphere $= \frac{4}{3}\pi r^3 = \frac{4}{3} \times \pi \times 3.2^3$ *[1 mark]*
       $= 137.258... = 137.3$ cm^3 (1 d.p.) *[1 mark]*
   [2 marks available in total — as above]

b) E.g. The container has a radius of 3.2 cm and a height
of $6 \times 3.2 = 19.2$ cm. It's volume is $\pi \times 3.2^2 \times 19.2$
$= 617.662... = 620$ cm^3 (2 s.f.), so Jeanine is correct.
[3 marks available — 1 mark for using a height of 19.2 cm,
1 mark for a correct method for calculating the volume of
the cylinder, 1 mark for the correct answer]

5   Volume of original cone $= \frac{1}{3} \times \pi \times 7^2 \times 24 = 392\pi$ cm^3
  Volume of removed cone $= \frac{1}{3} \times \pi \times 3^2 \times 4 = 12\pi$ cm^3
  Volume of frustum $= 392\pi - 12\pi = 380\pi$ cm^3
  [5 marks available — 1 mark for a correct method for finding
  the volume of a cone, 1 mark for 392π, 1 mark for 12π, 1 mark
  for subtracting the two volumes, 1 mark for the correct answer]

Pages 68-69: Rates of Flow

1   Volume of can $= \pi \times 3.8^2 \times 11.2 = 508.083...$ cm^3
  0.05 litres per second $= 0.05 \times 1000 = 50$ cm^3 per second
  So it will take $508.083... \div 50 = 10.161... \approx 10$ seconds
  [3 marks available — 1 mark for a correct method for
  calculating the volume, 1 mark for a correct method of
  using the rate of flow, 1 mark for the correct answer]

2   Volume of water $= 1.5$ m $\times 3$ m $\times 12$ m
       $= 150$ cm $\times 300$ cm $\times 1200$ cm
       $= 54\,000\,000$ cm^3
  27 litres per minute $= 27 \times 1000 = 27\,000$ cm^3 per minute
  $54\,000\,000 \div 27\,000 = 2000$ minutes ≈ 33 hours
  [3 marks available — 1 mark for a correct method for
  calculating the volume, 1 mark for a correct method of
  using the rate of flow, 1 mark for the correct answer]

3   Volume of ball $= \frac{4}{3} \times \pi \times 21^3 = 12\,348\pi$ cm^3
  $12\,348\pi$ cm$^3 = 12\,348\pi \div 1000 = 12.348\pi$ litres
  $12.348\pi \div 8 = 4.849... = 5$ seconds (1 s.f.)
  [3 marks available — 1 mark for a correct method for
  calculating the volume, 1 mark for a correct method of
  using the rate of flow, 1 mark for the correct answer]

4   Radius of cone $= 6.8 \div 2 = 3.4$ cm
  Height of cone $= 10 \div 2 = 5$ cm
  Volume of cone $= \frac{1}{3} \times \pi \times 3.4^2 \times 5 = 60.528...$ cm^3
  It takes $60.528... \div 2 = 30.264... \approx 30$ seconds for the sand timer
  to drain once. So Becky can measure approximately one minute
  by allowing the sand timer to drain twice.
  [4 marks available — 1 mark for 3.4 cm and 5 cm, 1 mark for a
  correct method for calculating the volume of one cone, 1 mark
  for a correct calculation of how long it takes the timer to drain
  once, 1 mark for the correct conclusion]

5 a) The funnel has a width of 2 m $= 200$ cm and a height of 3 m
  $= 300$ cm. So its volume is $\frac{1}{3} \times 200^2 \times 300 = 4\,000\,000$ cm^3.
  $4\,000\,000 \div 120 = 33\,333.3...$ seconds $= 9.26$ hours (2 d.p.)
  [3 marks available — 1 mark for a correct method for
  calculating the volume, 1 mark for a correct method of
  using the rate of flow, 1 mark for the correct answer]

b) 2 hours $= 7200$ seconds
120 cm$^3 \times 7200 = 864\,000$ cm^3 *[1 mark]*
$864\,000 \div 946 = 913.331...$
     $= 900$ bags *[1 mark]* (to the nearest 100)
[2 marks available in total — as above]

Section Six — Angles and Geometry

Pages 70-71: Loci and Construction

1

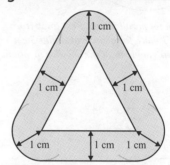

[2 marks available — 2 marks for arcs with a radius of 1 cm
centred at each vertex of the triangle, parallel lines 1 cm away
from each side of the triangle and correct area shaded,
otherwise 1 mark for either correct arcs or correct parallel lines]
You'll still get the marks if you are within 1 mm of the
correct measurements.

2

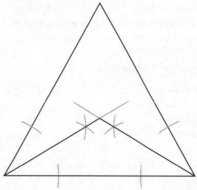

[3 marks available — 1 mark for each correct angle bisector,
1 mark for extending the bisectors to form a triangle]
You could have bisected two sides of the equilateral triangle,
then extended lines from the corners opposite each midpoint.

106

3

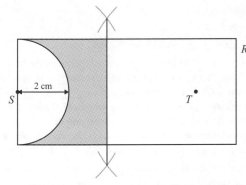

[4 marks available — 1 mark for a semicircle of radius 2 cm centred at S, 1 mark for accurate perpendicular bisector, 1 mark for construction marks, 1 mark for shading the correct region]

4

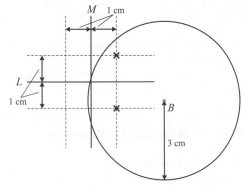

[3 marks available — 1 mark for parallel lines 1 cm away from either side of lines L and M, 1 mark for a circle of radius 3 cm centred at B, 1 mark for identifying both of the possible locations]

5

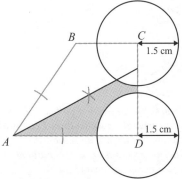

[5 marks available — 1 mark for construction marks on AD and AB for angle bisector at DAB, 1 mark for correct angle bisector at angle DAB, 1 mark for each circle with radius of 1.5 cm centred at C and D, 1 mark for the correct shading]

Pages 72-73: Pythagoras' Theorem

1   $(AC)^2 = 15^2 + 8^2$ *[1 mark]*
   $= 225 + 64 = 289$ *[1 mark]*
   $AC = \sqrt{289} = 17$ cm *[1 mark]*
   [3 marks available in total — as above]

2   $7^2 = 2^2 + (\text{height})^2$ *[1 mark]*
   $(\text{height})^2 = 7^2 - 2^2 = 49 - 4 = 45$ *[1 mark]*
   $\text{height} = \sqrt{45} = 6.708... = 6.7$ m (1 d.p.) *[1 mark]*
   [3 marks available in total — as above]

3   $RS = 20$ cm $\div 4 = 5$ cm *[1 mark]*
   $(RC)^2 = 5^2 - 4^2 = 25 - 16 = 9$ *[1 mark]*
   $RC = \sqrt{9} = 3$ cm *[1 mark]*
   $RT = RC + CT = 2 \times RC = 2 \times 3 = 6$ cm *[1 mark]*
   [4 marks available in total — as above]

4   No *[1 mark]*
   A right-angled triangle will always satisfy Pythagoras' theorem. However $5^2 + 12^2 = 25 + 144 = 169$
   and $14^2 = 196$, so the triangle is not possible. *[1 mark]*
   [2 marks available in total — as above]

5   As $BCDE$ is a square, $BC = BE = 12$ m. *[1 mark]*
   Triangles ABF and AFE are identical, so $BF = FE$
   and $BF = BE \div 2 = 12$ m $\div 2 = 6$ m. *[1 mark]*
   $10^2 = 6^2 + (AF)^2$ *[1 mark]*
   $(AF)^2 = 10^2 - 6^2 = 100 - 36 = 64$
   $AF = \sqrt{64} = 8$ m *[1 mark]*
   [4 marks available in total — as above]

6   Using $AE : ED = 1 : 3$, $AE = 27$ cm $\div 3 = 9$ cm *[1 mark]*
   $15^2 = (BE)^2 + 9^2$ *[1 mark]*
   $(BE)^2 = 15^2 - 9^2 = 225 - 81 = 144$
   $BE = \sqrt{144} = 12$ cm *[1 mark]*
   Area of parallelogram $= (9 + 27) \times 12 = 36 \times 12$
   $ = 432$ cm^2 *[1 mark]*
   [4 marks available in total — as above]

Pages 74-76: Trigonometry

1   $\sin x = \dfrac{O}{H}$

   $\sin 57° = \dfrac{m}{8}$ *[1 mark]*

   $8 \times \sin 57° = m$
   $m = 6.7093... = 6.7$ cm (1 d.p.) *[1 mark]*
   [2 marks available in total — as above]

2   a)   He has used the wrong formula for $\cos x$,

   it should be $\cos x = \dfrac{A}{H}$ *[1 mark]*

   The correct value of $\cos x = \dfrac{4}{5} = 0.8$ *[1 mark]*

   [2 marks available in total — as above]

   b) $x = \cos^{-1}(0.8) = 36.8698... = 36.9°$ (1 d.p.) *[1 mark]*

3   $\sin x = \dfrac{O}{A}$

   $\sin x = \dfrac{4}{7}$ *[1 mark]*

   $x = \sin^{-1}\left(\dfrac{4}{7}\right)$

   $x = 34.8499... = 34.8°$ (1 d.p.) *[1 mark]*
   [2 marks available in total — as above]

4   a) $\sin 60° + \cos 30° = \dfrac{\sqrt{3}}{2} + \dfrac{\sqrt{3}}{2} = \sqrt{3}$

   [2 marks available — 2 marks for correct answer, otherwise 1 mark for correct value of sin 60° or cos 30°]

   b) $4\cos 60° + \sin 90° = \left(4 \times \dfrac{1}{2}\right) + 1 = 3$

   [2 marks available — 2 marks for correct answer, otherwise 1 mark for correct value of cos 60° or sin 90°]

   c) $3\tan 45° - 4\sin 30° = (3 \times 1) - \left(4 \times \dfrac{1}{2}\right) = 3 - 2 = 1$

   [2 marks available — 2 marks for correct answer, otherwise 1 mark for correct value of tan 45° or sin 30°]

5   $\tan x = \dfrac{O}{A}$

   $\tan x = \dfrac{2\sqrt{3}}{2} = \sqrt{3}$ *[1 mark]*

   $x = \tan^{-1}(\sqrt{3})$
   $x = 60°$ *[1 mark]*
   [2 marks available — as above]

6   Using $CD : BC = 1 : 2$, $BC = 2 \times 2.5$ cm $= 5$ cm *[1 mark]*
   $ABCD$ is a rectangle, so $BC = AD = 5$ cm.

   ADC is a right-angled triangle and $\tan x = \dfrac{O}{A}$, so

   $\tan x = \dfrac{2.5}{5} = 0.5$ *[1 mark]*

   $x = \tan^{-1}(0.5)$
   $x = 26.565...° = 26.6°$ (1 d.p.) *[1 mark]*
   [3 marks available in total — as above]

7   AO and OC are radii of the circle, so $AO = OC = \sqrt{2}$ cm
and $AC = 2 \times \sqrt{2} = 2\sqrt{2}$ cm *[1 mark]*

$\cos x = \dfrac{A}{H}$

$\cos 33° = \dfrac{AB}{2\sqrt{2}}$ *[1 mark]*

$AB = \cos 33° \times 2\sqrt{2}$
$AB = 2.372... = 2.4$ cm (1 d.p.) *[1 mark]*
[3 marks available in total — as above]

8   Angle BAC + angle $BCA = 180° - 90° = 90°$. *[1 mark]*
$90° \div (3 + 7) = 9°$, so angle $BAC = 3 \times 9° = 27°$ *[1 mark]*

$\tan x = \dfrac{O}{A}$

$\tan 27° = \dfrac{BC}{17}$ *[1 mark]*

$BC = \tan 27° \times 17$
$BC = 8.661... = 8.7$ cm (1 d.p.) *[1 mark]*
[4 marks available in total — as above]

Pages 77-78: Vectors

1   a) $\mathbf{u} = \begin{pmatrix} 2 \\ 1 \end{pmatrix}$ *[1 mark]*, $\mathbf{v} = \begin{pmatrix} 0 \\ 2 \end{pmatrix}$ *[1 mark]*
[2 marks available in total — as above]

b)   i) $\begin{pmatrix} 2 \\ 1 \end{pmatrix} - 4 \times \begin{pmatrix} 0 \\ 2 \end{pmatrix} = \begin{pmatrix} 2 \\ 1 \end{pmatrix} - \begin{pmatrix} 0 \\ 8 \end{pmatrix} = \begin{pmatrix} 2 \\ -7 \end{pmatrix}$ *[1 mark]*

ii) $3 \times \begin{pmatrix} 2 \\ 1 \end{pmatrix} + \dfrac{1}{2} \times \begin{pmatrix} 0 \\ 2 \end{pmatrix} = \begin{pmatrix} 6 \\ 3 \end{pmatrix} + \begin{pmatrix} 0 \\ 1 \end{pmatrix} = \begin{pmatrix} 6 \\ 4 \end{pmatrix}$ *[1 mark]*

2   a) $\overrightarrow{BC} = -\overrightarrow{CB} = -(-\mathbf{b}) = \mathbf{b}$
$\overrightarrow{AC} = \overrightarrow{AB} + \overrightarrow{BC}$ *[1 mark]*
$= 2\mathbf{a} + \mathbf{b}$ *[1 mark]*
[2 marks available in total — as above]

b) $ABCD$ is a parallelogram, so $\overrightarrow{AB} = \overrightarrow{DC}$
and $\overrightarrow{DM} = \dfrac{1}{2}\overrightarrow{DC} = \dfrac{1}{2}\overrightarrow{AB}$. *[1 mark]*

$\overrightarrow{DM} = \dfrac{1}{2} \times 2\mathbf{a} = \mathbf{a}$ *[1 mark]*

[2 marks available in total — as above]

c) $ABCD$ is a parallelogram, so $\overrightarrow{DA} = \overrightarrow{CB}$
$\overrightarrow{MA} = \overrightarrow{MD} + \overrightarrow{DA}$ *[1 mark]*
$= -\overrightarrow{DM} + \overrightarrow{CB}$
$= -\mathbf{a} - \mathbf{b}$ *[1 mark]*
[2 marks available in total — as above]

3   a) $-2\mathbf{s}$ *[1 mark]*

b) $\mathbf{r} + \mathbf{r} + \mathbf{s} = 2\mathbf{r} + \mathbf{s}$ *[1 mark]*

c) $\overrightarrow{BC} = \overrightarrow{BA} + \overrightarrow{AC} = -\overrightarrow{AB} + \overrightarrow{AC}$
$= -(-2\mathbf{s}) + (2\mathbf{r} + \mathbf{s}) = 2\mathbf{r} + 3\mathbf{s}$ *[1 mark]*

This is what the vectors look like:

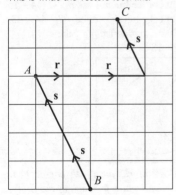

4   a) $\overrightarrow{AS} = \overrightarrow{AC} + \overrightarrow{CS}$ *[1 mark]*
$= -\overrightarrow{CA} + \dfrac{1}{2}\overrightarrow{CB}$ *[1 mark]*
$= -(-\mathbf{c} - 3\mathbf{d}) + \dfrac{1}{2}(2\mathbf{c} + 2\mathbf{d})$
$= \mathbf{c} + 3\mathbf{d} + \mathbf{c} + \mathbf{d} = 2\mathbf{c} + 4\mathbf{d}$ *[1 mark]*
[3 marks available in total — as above]

b) $2 \times \begin{pmatrix} -1 \\ 3 \end{pmatrix} + 4 \times \begin{pmatrix} 4 \\ 2 \end{pmatrix} = \begin{pmatrix} -2 \\ 6 \end{pmatrix} + \begin{pmatrix} 16 \\ 8 \end{pmatrix} = \begin{pmatrix} 14 \\ 14 \end{pmatrix}$ *[1 mark]*

Section Seven — Probability and Statistics

Pages 79-80: Probability Experiments

1   a) $150 - 63 = 87$ and $\dfrac{87}{150} = 0.58$ *[1 mark]*

b)   E.g. the coin may be biased *[1 mark]*

2   Relative frequency of Jan winning $= 1 - 0.17 - 0.53 = 0.3$
Expected number of times Jan wins $= 60 \times 0.3 = 18$
[2 marks available — 1 mark for calculating the correct relative frequency, 1 mark for the correct answer]

3   a)

Letter	A	B	C	D	E
Frequency	10	18	16	12	24
Relative frequency	0.125	0.225	0.2	0.15	0.3

[2 marks available — 2 marks if all entries are correct, otherwise 1 mark if at least 2 entries are correct]

b)   Estimate of the probability of landing on a letter other than E $= 1 - 0.3 = 0.7$. Estimate of the number of times landing on a letter other than E $= 120 \times 0.7 = 84$.
[2 marks available — 1 mark for a correct method of estimating the probability, 1 mark for the correct answer]
You could also have done 120 × 0.3 = 36, 120 − 36 = 84.

4   a)   Elyse: Total number of games played $= 16 + 34 = 50$
            Relative frequency of winning $= 16 \div 50 = 0.32$
     Nige: Total number of games played $= 27 + 13 = 40$
            Relative frequency of winning $= 27 \div 40 = 0.675$
[3 marks available — 3 marks for both correct, otherwise 2 marks for one correct, or 1 mark for calculating the total number of games played against either friend]

b)   The probability for Elyse is the more reliable estimate, as there were a greater number of games played than against Nige. *[1 mark]*

5   a)

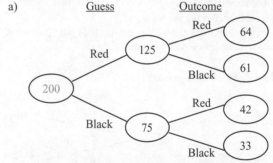

[2 marks available — 1 mark for correct numbers for the guesses, 1 mark for correct numbers for the outcomes]

b)   Lin guessed correctly $64 + 33 = 97$ *[1 mark]* out of 200 times,
so an estimate of the probability is $\dfrac{97}{200} = 0.485$ *[1 mark]*
[2 marks available in total — as above]

Pages 81-82: The AND/OR Rules

1   Total number of names in the hat $= 23 + 2 = 25$
P(Nancy or Trevor winning)
    $=$ P(Nancy winning) + P(Trevor winning)
    $= \dfrac{1}{25} + \dfrac{1}{25}$ *[1 mark]* $= \dfrac{2}{25}$ or 0.08 *[1 mark]*
[2 marks available in total — as above]

2   Total number of marbles $= 1 + 3 + 5 = 9$
P(Red marble) $= \dfrac{1}{9}$ *[1 mark]*, so the probability that two people in a row pick a red marble is $\dfrac{1}{9} \times \dfrac{1}{9} = \dfrac{1}{81}$ *[1 mark]*
[2 marks available in total — as above]

108

3 a) P(1 or 6) = P(1) + P(6)
     = 0.2 + 0.1 *[1 mark]*
     = 0.3 *[1 mark]*
  [2 marks available in total — as above]

b) P(Haley rolling a 1 or 6) = $\frac{2}{6}$ *[1 mark]*
P(Haley and Kim rolling a 1 or 6) = $\frac{2}{6}$ × 0.3 *[1 mark]*
         = 0.1 (or $\frac{1}{10}$) *[1 mark]*
[3 marks available in total — as above]

4 P(Brownie on Tuesday) = 0.05 × 2 = 0.1
P(Brownie on Wednesday) = 0.1 × 2 = 0.2
P(Brownie on Thursday) = 0.2 × 2 = 0.4
P(Brownie on Friday) = 0.4 × 2 = 0.8
P(No brownie on Friday) = 1 − P(Brownie on Friday)
        = 1 − 0.8
        = 0.2
P(Brownie on Thursday but not Friday) = 0.4 × 0.2
           = 0.08

[3 marks available in total — 1 mark for finding the probability of a brownie on Thursday, 1 mark for finding the probability of no brownie on Friday, 1 mark for the correct answer]

5 P(Spinner A landing on 4) = $\frac{1}{4}$, P(Spinner B landing on 4) = $\frac{1}{8}$
P(Spinner A and Spinner B landing on 4) = $\frac{1}{4}$ × $\frac{1}{8}$ = $\frac{1}{32}$
Estimate for the number of times that
both spinners land on 4 = 160 × $\frac{1}{32}$ = 5

[4 marks available — 1 mark for 1/4, 1 mark for 1/8, 1 mark for multiplying to get 1/32, 1 mark for the correct answer]

6 P(Alex missing the bullseye)
 = 1 − P(Alex hitting the bullseye) = 1 − 0.6 = 0.4 *[1 mark]*
P(Kari missing the bullseye)
 = 1 − P(Kari hitting the bullseye) = 1 − 0.3 = 0.7 *[1 mark]*
P(Both missing the bullseye)
 = P(Alex missing the bullseye) × P(Kari missing the bullseye)
 = 0.4 × 0.7 = 0.28 *[1 mark]*
So P(At least one hitting the bullseye)
 = 1 − P(Both missing the bullseye) = 1 − 0.28 = 0.72 *[1 mark]*
[4 marks available in total — as above]

Pages 83-84: Tree Diagrams

1 a)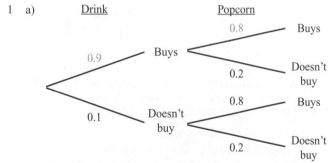

[2 marks available — 1 mark for the correct probability for a drink, 1 mark for the correct probabilities for popcorn]
b) P(Popcorn but not a drink) = 0.1 × 0.8 *[1 mark]*
        = 0.08 *[1 mark]*
[2 marks available in total — as above]

2 a)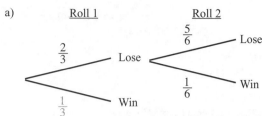

[2 marks available — 1 mark for the correct probability for first roll, 1 mark for the correct probabilities for second roll]

b) P(Winning on roll 2) = $\frac{2}{3}$ × $\frac{1}{6}$ *[1 mark]* = $\frac{1}{9}$
P(Winning) = P(Winning on roll 1) + P(Winning on roll 2)
    = $\frac{1}{3}$ + $\frac{1}{9}$ *[1 mark]*
    = $\frac{4}{9}$ *[1 mark]*

[3 marks available in total — as above]
You'd get the marks and the same answer by correctly working out 1 − P(Losing).

3 E.g. The probability that the first counter is not red is wrong (it should be 0.55). The labels 'Red' and 'Not red' on the top two branches for the second counter are in the wrong order.
[2 marks available — 1 mark for stating that the probability that the 1st counter is not red is wrong, or stating that the probabilities for the 1st counter don't add up to one, 1 mark for recognising that the labels (or the probabilities) for the 2nd counter are in the wrong order]

4 a)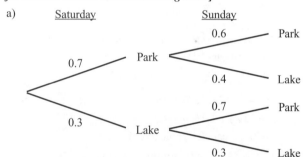

[2 marks available — 1 mark for the correct probabilities for Saturday, 1 mark for the correct probabilities for Sunday]
b) P(Park on both days) = 0.7 × 0.6 = 0.42 *[1 mark]*
P(Lake on both days) = 0.3 × 0.3 = 0.09 *[1 mark]*
P(Same on both days) = 0.42 + 0.09 = 0.51 *[1 mark]*
[3 marks available in total — as above]

Pages 85-86: Sets and Venn Diagrams

1 a) Number who bought coffee but not cake: 59 − 44 = 15
Number who bought cake but not coffee: 67 − 44 = 23
Number who bought neither coffee nor cake:
100 − 44 − 15 − 23 = 18
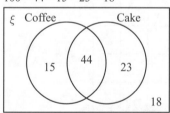

[3 marks available — 3 marks for a fully correct Venn diagram, otherwise lose 1 mark for each of the first three incorrect values]
b) 15 + 23 = 38 customers *[1 mark]* bought coffee or cake, but not both. So the probability is $\frac{38}{100}$ = 0.38. *[1 mark]*
[2 marks available in total — as above]

Answers

2 a)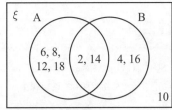

[3 marks available — 3 marks for a fully correct Venn diagram, otherwise lose 1 mark for each of the first three incorrect values]

b) $\xi = \{\,2, 4, 6, 8, 10, 12, 14, 16, 18\,\}$ has 9 elements
$A \cup B = \{\,2, 4, 6, 8, 12, 14, 16, 18\,\}$ has 8 elements *[1 mark]*

So the probability is $\frac{8}{9}$ *[1 mark]*

[2 marks available in total — as above]

3 a) 12 people own a cat and a dog, but not a hamster. *[1 mark]*

So the probability is $\frac{12}{100} = 0.12$ *[1 mark]*

[2 marks available in total — as above]

b) $10 + 7 + 6 + 17 = 40$ people own a hamster. This is more than the 23 people who own none of the pets, so yes — he's correct.
[2 marks available — 1 mark for calculating that 40 people own a hamster, 1 mark for the correct conclusion]

c) E.g. the cat or dog owners that also own a hamster have been added into the universal set instead of into the other parts of the diagram where they belong. *[1 mark]*

Pages 87-88: Mean, Median and Mode

1 Total number of fouls = 5 + 12 + 16 + 24 + 24 + 27
$\qquad\qquad$ + 28 + 32 + 36 + 38 + 44 = 286
Mean number of fouls = 286 ÷ 11 = 26
[2 marks available — 1 mark for a correct method of calculating the mean, 1 mark for the correct answer]

2 a) Range = 7.3 − 5.6 = 1.7 kg *[1 mark]*
E.g. the range is a good reflection of the spread of the data because there are no outliers. *[1 mark]*
[2 marks available in total — as above]

b) Total mass = 5.6 + 5.9 + 6.2 + 6.5 + 6.8 + 7.1 + 7.3
$\qquad\qquad$ = 45.4 kg
Mean mass = 45.4 ÷ 7 = 6.485... = 6.5 kg (1 d.p.)
[2 marks available — 1 mark for a correct method of calculating the mean, 1 mark for the correct answer]

3 a) x must be the highest or lowest value, otherwise the range would not be 29 (it would be 28 − 13 = 15). It can't be the lowest value, because it would have to be negative, so x = lowest number + range = 13 + 29 = 42 *[1 mark]*
The median m is the middle value, so it doesn't affect the range.

b) Total = mean × number of values = 22 × 7 = 154 *[1 mark]*
25 + 13 + 14 + 28 + 15 + 42 = 137
So m = 154 − 137 = 17 *[1 mark]*
[2 marks available in total — as above]
If the value you found for m isn't in the middle, then you know it must be wrong.

4 a) E.g. You can't tell if the median height will have changed, because you don't know enough data values. *[1 mark]*

b) Group A:
$\quad$ Old total height = 127 × 5 = 635
$\quad$ New total height = 635 − 125 = 510 *[1 mark]*
$\quad$ New mean = 510 ÷ 4 = 127.5 cm *[1 mark]*
Group B:
$\quad$ Old total height = 131 × 5 = 655
$\quad$ New total height = 655 + 125 = 780 *[1 mark]*
$\quad$ New mean = 780 ÷ 6 = 130 cm *[1 mark]*
[4 marks available in total — as above]

5 Old mean = 245 ÷ 7 = 35 *[1 mark]*
New mean = 35 + 5 = 40, so
New total age = 40 × 5 = 200 *[1 mark]*
The combined age of the two people who left is 245 − 200 = 45
[1 mark], so they must be 22 and 23 *[1 mark]*
[4 marks available in total — as above]

Pages 89-90: Grouped Frequency Tables

1 a) $8 < l \le 10$ *[1 mark]*

b) Total frequency = 11 + 24 + 15 + 10 = 60
The median is in position (60 + 1) ÷ 2 = 30.5,
so it's in the class $8 < l \le 10$.
[2 marks available — 1 mark for a correct method to find the position of the median, 1 mark for the correct answer]

2 a) Estimate of range = 45 − 20 = 25 g *[1 mark]*

b) (31 + 1) ÷ 2 = 16
So January's median is in the class $30 < m \le 35$.
(28 + 1) ÷ 2 = 14.5
So February's median is in the class $25 < m \le 30$.
So no, John is not correct — the median for February must be lower than the median for January.
[3 marks available — 1 mark for identifying the class containing the median for January, 1 mark for identifying the class containing the median for February, 1 mark for stating that John is not correct]

3

Time	Freq	Mid-interval value	Freq × Mid-interval
$0 < t \le 2$	6	1	6 × 1 = 6
$2 < t \le 4$	9	3	9 × 3 = 27
$4 < t \le 6$	6	5	6 × 5 = 30
$6 < t \le 8$	3	7	3 × 7 = 21
$8 < t \le 10$	1	9	1 × 9 = 9
Total:	25	—	93

Estimate of mean = 93 ÷ 25 = 3.72 minutes
[3 marks available — 1 mark for correctly estimating the total time, 1 mark for dividing total time by total frequency, 1 mark for the correct answer]

4 a)

Height	Freq	Mid-interval value	Freq × Mid-interval
$0 < h \le 15$	5	(0 + 15) ÷ 2 = 7.5	5 × 7.5 = 37.5
$15 < h \le 30$	9	(15 + 30) ÷ 2 = 22.5	9 × 22.5 = 202.5
$30 < h \le 45$	10	(30 + 45) ÷ 2 = 37.5	10 × 37.5 = 375
$45 < h \le 60$	6	(45 + 60) ÷ 2 = 52.5	6 × 52.5 = 315
Total:	30	—	930

Estimate of mean = 930 ÷ 30 = 31 cm
[4 marks available — 1 mark for all mid-interval values correct, 1 mark for correctly estimating the total height, 1 mark for dividing total height by total frequency, 1 mark for the correct answer]

b) E.g. Audrey could use more classes with smaller intervals.
[1 mark for a correct comment]

Formulas in the Exams

GCSE Maths uses a lot of formulas — that's no lie. You'll be scuppered if you start trying to answer a question without the proper formula to start you off. Thankfully, CGP is here to explain all things formula-related.

You're Given these Formulas

Fortunately, those lovely, cuddly examiners give you some of the formulas you need to use.

> **For a sphere radius r, or a cone with base radius r, slant height l and vertical height h:**
>
> Volume of sphere $= \dfrac{4}{3}\pi r^3$ Volume of cone $= \dfrac{1}{3}\pi r^2 h$
>
> Surface area of sphere $= 4\pi r^2$ Curved surface area of cone $= \pi r l$

And, actually, that's your lot I'm afraid. As for the rest...

Learn All The Other Formulas

Sadly, there are a load of formulas which you're expected to be able to remember straight out of your head. There isn't space to write them all out below, but here are the highlights:

Area of parallelogram = base × vertical height

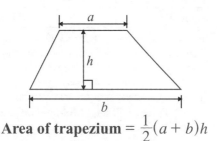

Area of trapezium $= \dfrac{1}{2}(a + b)h$

Exterior angle of regular polygon $= \dfrac{360°}{n}$

Sum of interior angles of any polygon $= (n - 2) \times 180°$

where n is the number of sides

For a circle with radius r:

Circumference $= 2\pi r$ Area $= \pi r^2$

Volume of prism = cross-sectional area × length

Volume of cylinder = area of circle × height = $\pi r^2 h$

Surface area of cylinder $= 2\pi r h + 2\pi r^2$

Compound Growth and Decay:

$$N = N_0\left(1 + \dfrac{r}{100}\right)^n$$

where N = total amount, N_0 = initial amount, r = percentage change and n = number of days/weeks/years etc.

Area of sector $= \dfrac{x°}{360°} \times$ Area of full circle

Length of Arc $= \dfrac{x°}{360°} \times$ Circumference of full circle

For a right-angled triangle:

Pythagoras' theorem: $a^2 + b^2 = c^2$

Trigonometry ratios:

$\sin x = \dfrac{O}{H}$, $\cos x = \dfrac{A}{H}$, $\tan x = \dfrac{O}{A}$

Compound Measures:

Speed $= \dfrac{\text{Distance}}{\text{Time}}$ Density $= \dfrac{\text{Mass}}{\text{Volume}}$ Pressure $= \dfrac{\text{Force}}{\text{Area}}$